The Traveling Tea Ladies
Death in Dallas

Melanie O'Hara-Salyers

Little Creek Books

A division of Mountain Girl Press
Bristol, VA

Little Creek Books

A division of Mountain Girl Press
Bristol, VA

This is a work of fiction. Any resemblance to actual persons, either living or dead is entirely coincidental. All names, characters, and events are the product of the author's imagination.

The Traveling Tea Ladies™
Death in Dallas

Little Creek Books
Published 2010

Cover art by Pam Keaton
www.pamkeaton.com

You may contact the publisher at:
Little Creek Books
A Division of Mountain Girl Press
P.O. Box 17013
Bristol, VA 24209-7013
E-mail: publisher@littlecreekbooks.com

ISBN: 978-0-9843192-4-4

Acknowledgements

Endless thanks to my husband, Keith, my real-life "Shane Spencer." Thank you for always being my "Biggest Fan" and making all my dreams come true and for pushing me to finish this book.

To my children, Olivia and Charlie who make my heart sing! I so love being your Mom and have enjoyed every age and stage of your life. I am fiercely proud of the smart, beautiful and motivated young adults growing up before my eyes! Thank you both for allowing me to base a character on you.

To Josh, who allowed room in his heart for me to love him like my own. I'm very proud of your achievements and the man you have become!

To my Mom, Judy O'Hara-King, who always encouraged me to write and watched endless hours of my dance performances and plays in our kitchen.

To my Dad, Jim O'Hara, who carefully edited my high school writing and stressed the importance of a good education.

Thank you to Greg O'Hara for being a great brother and even better Uncle.

Thank you to my publisher, Tammy Robinson Smith, for "getting it" and allowing me creative freedom. Thank you for your continued support!

Thank you to Pam Keaton for making "the ladies" come to life! You are truly a gifted artist!

A Letter To The Reader

Dear Friend,

I often get asked when and how I began writing and I have to laugh thinking back to the plays I wrote to raise money for the Jerry Lewis Muscular Dystrophy Telethon. Instead of selling lemonade or a bake sale, I involved all the kids on our block in elaborate productions which we rehearsed for days. I soon learned that attention spans are short when you are seven years old and kids would rather ride bikes or play with their Barbie's instead of rehearse, so we never actually made it to the final performance. But I wrote one every summer and practiced all the parts myself, usually roping my brother, Greg, into it!

Growing up, I always had a pot of tea with my mother after school and one of our favorite things to do when we traveled was to visit tea rooms. It was only after my summer living abroad in London studying international communications that I experienced authentic Afternoon Tea and my passion for tea was truly ignited! I knew I wanted to return to the states, open my own tea business and share my love of tea with everyone. Many years later, with much encouragement and support from my husband, Keith, and our children, the dream began with the opening of Miss Melanie's Tea Room, the addition of our online business- Smokey Mountain Coffee, Herb and Tea Company and eventually expanding into consulting and training tea professionals all over the U.S. with The Tea Academy.

Many of the recipes I feature in this book are tried and true in my tea room and come from my grandmothers, Ellen and Essie. Grandma Ellen was a wonderful baker and her cheese cake was legendary as well as her cookies. My grandmother, Essie, actually owned her own restaurant and allowed me to take guest's orders at the early age of three! Of course, one of her servers was standing by to make sure the order was turned into the kitchen correctly, but I can vividly remember how exciting it was to visit her at her restaurant.

I hope you enjoy taking this journey with me and glimpsing life in a small East Tennessee town. It doesn't get much better than looking out your window at the splendor of autumn leaves in hues of burnt orange and gold; the panoramic view of the snow capped Smokey Mountains in winter or the countryside scattered with blooming Dogwoods and Redbud trees in the spring. I hope you will find a comfortable chair to snuggle up in, make a hot pot of tea or a pitcher of iced tea and join Amelia and her friends on their tea adventures!

I invite you to join our "Traveling Tea Ladies Society" and share your own personal tea adventures and photos with us! There will be opportunities for you to attend upcoming book signings, tea tastings, tea tours and more. Please visit www.TheTraveling TeaLadiesSociety.com to register. I would love to hear from you!

Until Our Next Pot of Tea,
Melanie

Dedication

For Essie
For showing us unconditional love,
teaching us the power of forgiveness,
and making each of her grandchildren feel
as though we are her favorite!
I love you very much.

Chapter One

It had been a long, hot and humid summer in Dogwood Cove, Tennessee. It was the kind of summer that made the record books as the mercury soared! This was the third year in a row that the area had suffered a record drought. It had taken a toll on the strawberry, pumpkin, apple and tomato crops in the area, which would mean a decrease in tourists during Dogwood Cove's Fall Apple Festival.

Putting the tea room up for sale was something I never imagined I would be doing. I loved every inch of this regal pink beauty. Built in 1904, it had housed Dogwood Cove's first police chief and his seven children. Past families that had lived in the home had shared with me photos and tales of sliding down the great curved banister in the entry way and had showed me the coal shoot at the back of the house where the coal trucks made deliveries to heat the eight fireplaces. It was the second house built on the street back when the road had been graveled, and it was listed with The National Register of Historic Buildings.

I was not looking forward to packing up all the antiques and belongings that filled our Victorian tea room. Any movement that required an ounce of exertion was sure to make beads of sweat pop out on my forehead. Moving is always a trial, no matter what time of year you plan a move especially in late August!

"It's time to move on, Amelia," Shane conceded while taking another bite of my signature recipe peanut butter pie. He gently put his arm around my shoulder and gave me a loving squeeze. "I know how hard this decision is on you, but I now need your help in the business. Remember, starting the wholesale company was your idea to make work easier on you." He quickly wiped the chocolate traces from his mouth with a satisfied smile on his face.

"I know," I said as my eyes filled with tears. "But the tea room has been a part of me and part of Dogwood Cove for so long. I have made lasting friendships with so many people over the years." I tried to smile as tears continued to spill down my now splotchy and swollen face.

"You keep forgetting, honey," Shane reassured me. "We are not moving away. You will still get to see everyone around town and at all the committee meetings you are involved with! This is not goodbye. We are just moving the business in a different direction," he gently reminded me.

We had made the plan three years ago to begin a wholesale tea and coffee business on the side in the hopes that I could work more normal hours than The Pink Dogwood Tea Room currently allowed. Waking up at four o'clock in the morning to make freshly baked scones from scratch, my legendary quiche and a varied selection of desserts developed from my grandmother's recipes, had turned me into a sleep deprived zombie. Shane and I had a dream of continuing the tea business and working "smarter not harder!" Somehow I thought it would take much longer for the wholesale business to grow.

A large warehouse building and six full-time employees later, Smoky Mountain Coffee, Herb and Tea Company was in full swing. The time to transition had come. It was bitter sweet for me.

How was I going to break the news to everyone that we would be selling the tea room? After all, The Pink Dogwood Tea

Room was the central hub for all the ladies who loved to lunch and share afternoon tea. It would be next to impossible to add up all the young girls who had shared their Princess birthday teas over the years. We had several Red Hat chapters in our area and surrounding towns that loved to come to The Pink Dogwood. They were the mainstay of our business. Hopefully, whoever purchased the historic Victorian "Pink Lady" as we referred to her, would love it as much as I did!

"When are you going to let the girls know?" Shane asked.

He knew that would be the hardest part. It was our favorite gathering spot and how we all met in the first place. Who would have thought sharing a pot of tea could bring such different people so close together?

"Olivia is having us over at the farm tonight for a cook out. I really don't want to tell them, but I would hate for them to hear it through the real estate grapevine," I added with dread in my voice.

In a small southern town, news travels lightening fast. I could be assured this bit of news would travel like a rocket!

My friends and I are fondly known about town as "The Traveling Tea Ladies." We earned the nickname from all the escapades we've shared on our travels near and far. Somehow, we've always viewed life as one big tea party and manage to have fun whenever we're together.

We "Traveling Tea Ladies" recently returned from a "Tea Cruise" where we spent a week aboard a luxury cruise ship and enjoyed afternoon tea every day, cooking classes featuring tea as an ingredient, educational tea tastings, as well as classes from some of the leading speakers in the tea industry. We were only asked to leave the disco once when Cassandra had one too many "Tea-tinis," a tea infused vodka martini, and started doing the Macarena with the cruise director.

Cassandra Reynolds came from old money, the kind that comes from a third generation candy business old money. Her model-like thin frame and platinum blonde hair drew attention wherever she went. Of course, she always appeared in Dogwood Cove's "Best Dressed List," which is a most coveted title in this Tennessee mountain town. And she should! She could always be found in Paris and Milan during Fashion Week as she jetted about with the latest Hollywood "A List" friends.

Cassandra was just as much at home in her lakeside mansion in Tennessee with her politically connected husband, Doug, as she was in her homes in the Sonoma Valley, Palm Beach, and, of course, the town house in Paris. Doug may be the president of the family candy business, but Cassandra is the brains behind its recent success. After all, it was her brilliant idea of using her Hollywood connections to get Reynolds's Chocolates put in all the Oscar gift bags, a move that has re-launched the candy company's popularity.

Sarah McCaffrey is our local librarian. In comparison to Cassandra, she lives a very modest life in a small rental cottage at the outskirts of town. Unlike Cassandra, she wouldn't be caught dead in a hip hair salon or Hollywood premiere. She prefers her natural brunette hair cropped short and her glasses in "Sally Jesse Raphael" red. Her hard work ethic and creative ideas have helped her secure the committee chairperson position for this year's Dogwood Cove Apple Festival.

Sarah is a quiet, yet quirky addition to the group. Her outlandish outfits inspired by her latest "cause of the day," have often left many Dogwood Cove residents wondering, "*Where DOES she do her shopping?*" The children adore her and her story telling time at the library often times is a standing room only event with the toddler set because guests can be assured that she will wear a flamboyant costume to go along with her literary selection of the day!

Olivia Rivers is the red head in our group. Her love of barrel racing and all things related to horseback riding, including the occasional cowboy, resulted in building her dream farm, Riverbend Ranch. When most people meet Olivia, they would never assume she could rope a calf or haul bales of hay as well as any farm hand due to her petite height of five feet. But one full day of work around Riverbend Ranch and you know that she is all business! Her sometimes brash and sassy attitude can keep most people at bay, but anyone who truly knows Olivia would tell she has a heart the size of Texas.

And to round out the foursome of "The Traveling Tea Ladies" is me — Amelia Spencer, local tea expert and owner of The Pink Dogwood Tea Room. My passion for tea began during my college years when I studied abroad in London and it inspired me to create a haven for our local residents to experience authentic afternoon tea. I also teach etiquette lessons as well as children's cooking classes. My tea tasting classes have been so popular that we have a waiting list!

I've been married to my husband, Shane, for fifteen years and we have two beautiful children, Emma, who is fourteen, and Charlie, who is twelve. We lead a fairly calm life aside from the fact that we both own our own businesses, which are things that keep us working most of the time. It's been hard to juggle Emma's band performances, the kids' nightly homework review and Charlie's football practice schedule, not to mention his Saturday game days!

Most people who meet me would probably describe me as a down to earth and even tempered person. My wardrobe is rather tailored and classic, very blah in comparison to Sarah's carefree costumes. I usually have my shoulder length dark blonde hair twisted in a French knot or sleek pony tail to keep the health inspector happy during work hours. Besides tea, my other secret addictions are dark chocolate and my V.W. convertible bug, affectionately nicknamed "Lady Bug" for her red body and black rag top.

Tonight we are meeting at Riverbend Farm for Olivia's famous BBQ ribs. We Tennesseans like our sauce on the sweet side with a little brown sugar and molasses in it. Olivia was providing the ribs, and the rest of us were bringing the sides.

I was taking my Grandmother's antique deviled egg dish filled with our Southern staple for summer get-togethers: deviled eggs. I make mine in the traditional style with a little Dijon mustard, sweet pickle relish, a splash of red wine vinegar and mayonnaise. They were always a hit with everyone and I had brought a huge plastic container filled with plenty of back-ups. I also had a key lime pie in a cooler in back of "Lady Bug" along with a gallon of my secret recipe peach iced tea. That surprise would be for later.

"Hey, Amelia!" Olivia said through a cough as the thick smoke from her grill began to get the best of her. "I didn't hear you drive up!"

Olivia was wearing a pair of her favorite Wranglers and a turquoise scoop neck short sleeved blouse that contrasted beautifully with her red hair. She had on a pair of dangling amber beaded earrings, a feminine touch to this short statured cow girl.

"Boy, those ribs smell amazing," I stated.

"The ribs are coming along well," Olivia said wiping the sauce from her hands on a kitchen towel. "What have you been up to today?" she questioned.

"Well, I've got some news to share with you," I began to say.

"Wait a minute, wait a minute," Cassandra called out, her hands full of a pitcher of something icy. "I've brought to the party my own version of Lynchburg Lemonade."

In case you have never tried Lynchburg Lemonade, it is made with Jack Daniels and it has a real kick to it! It is one part Jack Daniels, one part triple sec, one part sour mix and four parts lemon-lime soda, long stemmed cherry optional. The Tennessee distillery is not too far a drive from Dogwood Cove and has always been a favorite destination for tourists to our fine

Volunteer state. Their "Tipsy Cakes" are always a best seller in the tea room gift shop.

Cassandra set down the pitcher and took a large Louis Vuitton tote bag off her shoulder. She began unwrapping and distributing elegant crystal high balls from her bag.

"Here you go, Livy!" she sang as she handed Olivia her lemonade. "Drink up dear and let's get this party started!"

"Nice outfit," smirked Olivia. How much did your country club get up cost you? She said.

"It's just Polo," Cassandra whined through her nose as she smoothed her white linen skirt and adjusted her hot pink cardigan sweater tied smartly around her shoulders. "Where did you get your outfit? Rodeos-R-Us?" she teased.

"You two really should be nicer to each other," piped up Sarah who was walking up to the bricked patio area. She was costumed in a short denim skirt, light brown suede vest with matching Pocahontas inspired fringed sandals with her hair fixed in two short brown braids. "I just love the view of the Smoky Mountains from your place, Olivia. I never get tired of looking at them!" she gushed.

She was right! The view was exceptional from Olivia's back porch and patio. The vistas everywhere in Dogwood Cove were breathtaking because the town was nestled in a valley surrounded by the ancient Smoky Mountains. Fall was always spectacular here, but spring was when the tourists would flock to our valley to photograph the pink and white blooms of our Dogwood trees, a truly beautiful sight to behold. The town's people had planted an extraordinary amount of trees back in the 1960s in hopes of becoming one of the most beautiful destinations in the South.

"Hey, Sarah," I jumped up and helped her with a rather large tray loaded down with all kinds of covered casserole dishes. "What have you got in here?"

"Oh, just my corn fritters, fried green tomatoes and potato salad," she announced, rather proud of herself.

"Gosh, Sarah," Cassandra said as she took another sip of her lemonade. "You make me look bad! All I cooked tonight were the cocktails."

Cassandra was a self-proclaimed kitchen screw up. Growing up in a lifestyle of privilege, she never really bothered to learn basic kitchen skills. What she did excel in perfecting was having all the right contacts. She must have had twelve caterers on speed dial, ready at a moment's notice. It was a well-known fact that for her last dinner party she flew in Oprah's latest chef from Chicago, just for an intimate party of eight. That got a little write up in our hometown paper, *The Dogwood Daily*.

"Don't worry, Cassandra!" Olivia yelled over the noise of sizzling ribs. "I have a mess of baked beans, and I am grilling corn on the cob too. We will have plenty of food."

Olivia loved taking charge of the grill as much as she loved taking charge of the horses and all the animals at the farm. It was a big leap for her to purchase the property for Riverbend Ranch, but it was a risk Olivia was willing to take.

Riverbend Ranch was not only a great place to horseback ride along the picturesque Tennessee River; it was also a therapeutic horseback riding center for kids with both physical and developmental challenges. There were only a handful of therapeutic riding centers in the U.S., and Olivia was proud to have nearly fifty students a week with an ever growing waiting list. If she could add more hours to her already long day and have more volunteer help, she might be able to accommodate all the children.

That "Volunteer Spirit" that earned our beautiful state its nickname was how all of us met. I was hosting a "thank you" tea at The Pink Dogwood for all the community volunteers. Sarah was in attendance for her work at the library, as well as the Dogwood Cove Apple Festival. Olivia was there for her therapeutic riding center, and Cassandra was there for her endowment of the arts. I happened to serve on the Apple Festival committee with Sarah. My daughter Emma was a volunteer at Riverbend Farm, and

I had met Cassandra when we had a cast after party at The Pink Dogwood following last holiday's *Nutcracker* performance of our Community Ballet Company. It was an auspicious meeting to say the least. We have been fast friends ever since!

"Let's set the tray over here," I suggested to Sarah. "I don't know how you carried this all by yourself!"

She smiled at me and gave me a quick hug as I set down her assortment of covered casseroles and snuck a corn fritter while they were still warm.

"Okay, Amelia. Spit it out," Cassandra demanded. "What was this big news I interrupted?"

"Well, hmm, first let's toast the evening," I stammered. Everyone grabbed their lemonade. "To the 'Traveling Tea Ladies' and our adventures together!" We noisily clanked our crystal highballs.

Olivia's ribs were set down in the center of the enormous trestle table. We sat on long benches on either side. The churning of the river washing over the rocks below us sounded like soothing music in the background.

"Do you mind if we dig in while you fill us in?" Olivia proceeded. If there's one thing I know about Olivia, she works up an appetite with her farm work. Some of her previous dates have quickly found out that she can eat them under the table and still keep her petite figure.

"Go ahead," I conceded. We were all hungry and the fried green tomatoes were particularly tempting that night. They are only available during the summer months and are a true delicacy.

"Sarah, you have outdone yourself tonight," Cassandra purred. "I don't understand why some man hasn't snatched you up!"

"Okay, Amelia." Olivia urged. "Out with it."

"All right," I paused as I fought back tears.

"What in the world is wrong?" Olivia demanded. "Did Shane do something? If he did, I will tie him to the stake!" She took another bite of the messy ribs.

9

We all remembered the last time one of Olivia's beau's had been caught necking with another woman in his pickup truck. Olivia had taken Carrie Underwood's latest ballad to heart and had left a nice indentation in the driver's side door. She was one not to be fooled with!

"Heavens no!" I exclaimed. If there was one thing I could count on besides these three ladies it was the rock steady support of my husband. We had been through a lot together over our fifteen year marriage, and we had a very strong foundation.

"Don't scare us like that," Sarah said breathlessly. "I couldn't handle it if you two broke up. I think I would just give up on men and dating all together."

Sarah had just ended a six month relationship with Jake White, a reporter for *The Dogwood Daily*. We all thought that maybe Jake's creative writing background and high intellect would be a good match for her. Sarah was not one to divulge the details of their break up. Who knows? Maybe they could still work it out!

"Y'all are so funny!" I told them. "It's not anything that serious. Shane and I are more than fine," I reassured them.

"You two make me sick," Cassandra piped in. "I wish Doug still looked at me that way. You guys look like you haven't ended the honeymoon phase yet."

Cassandra and Doug had been married close to ten years by now. They both had decided that children didn't fit into their lifestyle of country clubs, jet setting, and board rooms. They seemed to have a solid partnership both at home and at Reynolds's Candies. They made a good team. There were rumors that Doug would be calling in favors from his Hollywood "A list" friends if he should decide to run for Senate. Cassandra was pretty tight lipped about Doug's political prospects and I didn't ask. Even good friends have to respect each other's privacy.

"Get on with the news," Olivia murmured while finishing her third rib. "I am dying to know! Pass those deviled eggs this way."

"Okay, okay!" I said and held my breath for a brief second. "We are putting 'The Pink Lady' up for sale." All right, it was out. I had said it!

"What!" Olivia shouted. "Why? You're not moving are you?"

"No, no. We're not moving," I quickly replied.

"Why are you selling, then?" Sarah wondered. Her lip had begun to tremble ever so slightly.

"Well, the wholesale business has really taken off, and Shane needs my help," I informed them. It was something we planned all along, but it just happened a lot sooner than I thought it would."

"Can't he hire some more help?" Cassandra asked as she poured more lemonade into everyone's glasses. "I know of several qualified people who would be well suited to work at your tea and coffee business."

"Shane and I started Smoky Mountain Coffee, Herb and Tea Company so I wouldn't be working such long hours in the tea room," I said. "We are at the point now that I can let go of The Pink Dogwood and really focus on my passion—the tea! Y'all know Shane is all about the coffee. We complement each other well. It's really very exciting, but still, I will miss the day-to-day activities of the tea room."

Shane and I both had taken tea and coffee certification classes. I didn't know how to explain to the girls that operating the wholesale end of the business was all part of the dream we had when we opened The Pink Dogwood. It was a stepping stone for us. And I loved my guests! They were like family to me. I tried to make each person who walked through the doors feel as though I was entertaining them in my own home.

Sarah was dabbing her eyes and turning away to blow her nose with a tissue. I had no idea she would take the news so hard!

"Sarah, sweetheart," I reassured her as I rubbed her arm. "What's wrong? Why are you crying?

"You don't know what how much coming to The Pink Dogwood has meant to me over the years," Sarah said between hiccups. "I feel at peace and so centered when I am there. Who is going to care about everyone as much as you do?" she asked. By now she was sobbing.

"Sarah, calm down!" Olivia scolded. "Amelia should be the one who's crying! You know she puts her heart and soul into everything she makes there. I know I am going to miss your Grandmother's Key Lime pie!"

While we had been consoling Sarah, Olivia had finished her meal. She was ready for dessert. The only thing she loved more than ribs was satisfying that sweet tooth of hers.

"You did bring dessert, Amelia, didn't you?" Olivia asked with hope in her voice.

"I did more than that," I said. I also brought Shane's favorite organic Guatemalan coffee. Can I step inside and brew a pot, Livy?"

"I think I'm about ready for coffee and pie too," Cassandra said. "My offer still stands if you need some extra help at the warehouse."

"Thanks, Cassandra." I gave her a quick hug. "I am sure Shane and I will be expanding our staff in no time. I can't believe how fast the company has grown."

What began as a spinoff of The Pink Dogwood's gift shop had turned into a full scale business. First, it was an online store attached to our website, but we soon realized we were having a hard time keeping up with the orders that were coming in and not just from Dogwood Cove! The website had grown into its own independent business, and Shane had taken the plunge and left his thriving antique business to work full time developing Smoky Mountain Coffee, Herb and Tea Company. After all, he could still dabble with the antiques and they were selling well in the tea room. But Shane felt that if the online business was going to appeal to both men and women, "The Pink Dogwood

Coffee Herb and Tea Company" just didn't sound like a place where guys would want to buy their coffee and tea. It needed a more universally appealing name.

I took the pie out of the cooler and sliced four healthy pieces. A little dollop of my famous almond cream and a sliver of strawberry on top would make it perfect! I placed the pie and steaming mugs of coffee on one of Olivia's trays and joined the girls on the patio.

Sarah had composed herself by this time. I had no idea she would be the one to react the strongest. After a few bites of pie and the coffee to fortify us, we were laughing and cutting up as usual.

"Amelia," Olivia asked in her rather blunt way. "How much do you think you're going to ask for The Pink Dogwood?" She was not one to mince words.

Cassandra slapped her arm. "Olivia, you are so rude!" she snapped at her. "Do you always have to be so blunt and cut to the chase?

"Yes, I pride myself in the fact that I am blunt," Olivia replied. Her red headed temper was flaring a tiny bit. "I'm a business woman. This is a business decision. If anyone could help Amelia, it would be us," she continued.

I spoke up, "Olivia, you're right. I could use some good business advice right now. And no, I don't mind telling you how much I am going to ask for The Pink Dogwood. I am selling the business and building together. I will be happy to train whoever buys 'The Pink Lady.' And I will also be including my recipes, inventory, and website."

"You can get a good sum with that business arrangement," Cassandra said, shaking her head deep in thought. "I don't think you will have a problem selling. Have you selected a real estate agent yet?" She took another sip from her steaming mug of coffee.

"No, we haven't, "I told Cassandra. "I know who we're not using, that loud-mouthed, Sally Stokes, who nearly botched the deal when we were negotiating the purchase of the 'Pink Lady' to begin with. That was a nightmare! Plus, on a personal note, she drives me crazy!"

"Oh, yeah!" Olivia chimed in. "I know Sally Stokes. What a busy body. If there's one thing I can't stand, it is people who poke their nose where it doesn't belong," she added. She was getting ready to help herself to another slice of key lime pie.

"There's a lot more than one thing you can't stand, Olivia," Cassandra teased her. "Men who chew tobacco, people who drive while talking on their cell phones, people who park their shopping cart in the middle of the aisle so no one can pass around them. Shall I continue?" she teased.

"So, I have a few pet peeves," Olivia shrugged it off. "I like to think I am particular." She took a big bite of pie and smiled smugly at Cassandra.

"More like peculiar!" Cassandra slapped her knee and shrieked at her own joke. Don't let these two ladies fool you. Even though they go at it quite regularly, they are very fond of each other. Like some say, opposites attract.

"Well, I hate for all things to come to an end," I yawned, "but I've got an early start tomorrow at the tea room. We're hosting Rebecca Givens Princess Tea Party along with our regular Saturday crowd."

"Need some help, Amelia?" Sarah offered. "I am not scheduled at the library tomorrow, and you know how I love the kids' special events!"

She was finally smiling again, which I was glad to see.

"Yeah, that would be great, Sarah," I said. "Can you come as early as ten o'clock in the morning? I could use your help setting up for the party."

Sarah had a way with children, a way with her Southern cooking and a way with detailed decorating. If the lengths she went into creating her costume wardrobe were any indication, Sarah had quite a talent. Sometimes she got a bit carried away.

One time she tried to wear her hair in a bee-hive to complement the 60s vintage dress she had picked up at the "New to You" consignment boutique. Instead of retro, she looked more like a crazed fan at a *B-52s* concert! But much like Olivia, Sarah had a heart of gold. Children were her soft spot.

We all helped to clear and wash up the dishes before we packed up our gear and went our separate ways. I left Olivia the remaining slices of pie and the peach iced tea, which she gladly accepted. Tomorrow would hold its own worries and surprises. What I needed was a good night's sleep.

Chapter Two

"What did the girls think of the big news?" Shane asked bright and early the next morning. He was still in his slippers and bathrobe, but had voluntarily joined me in the wee hours of dawn out on our back porch so we could sneak some quality time in before both our days started.

I sipped from my warm tea cup and sighed as contentment washed over me. "This Darjeeling is some of the best we've tried," I told Shane. "What tea estate did you purchase this from?"

"Amelia, we can talk about tea later," Shane laughed. "Tell me the details. I bet Cassandra flipped out! Where is she going to entertain all her upper crust friends now?" he teased as he did his best imitation of Thurston Howell III from *Gilligan's Island*.

"Actually, it was Sarah who was the most upset." I filled him in on our conversation from the night before.

"Well, I am glad Sarah will be helping you today," he said. "There's no telling how many reservations were called in since you last checked your voice mail yesterday."

"You're right," I groaned. Saturday mornings were always a scramble of juggling reservations and calling to confirm seating times. And no matter how many scones I prepared, there never seemed to be enough! That's why I learned to make them ahead and freeze them so I could pop them into the oven if we should run short.

"I've got to run," I said and gave Shane a quick kiss goodbye. "Let's plan on seven o'clock for dinner tonight. We're having your favorite, pot roast. I've already put it in the crock pot. And before I forget, when Emma gets up, remind her that Julia's Mom is picking her up for a one o'clock movie and trip to the mall. I will pick them up at the mall entrance at 5:30 sharp."

Shane shook his head in the affirmative. "And tell Charlie that football practice is two o'clock today. You can still take him, right?" I asked.

"Get going. I've got it!" he playfully swatted my fanny.

"See you for dinner. Call me if you need me, okay?" I yelled over my shoulder.

I fired up "Lady Bug" and headed south for the short six-mile drive to work. It was only six o'clock in the morning, but already I could feel the humidity in the air. I played a little *Journey* on the C.D. player and sang along. Gosh, no one could sing like Steve Perry anymore!

Sufficiently charged up from my own personal rendition of *Separate Ways*, I was ready to tackle the messages waiting for me. I unlocked the back porch door, flipped on the lights and cranked up the A/C. I headed over to the telephone.

Not too bad. I had only five messages. The first was from the Givens Princess Party. They would be adding five more guests. Last minute changes in party numbers went along with the territory. I made a mental note-five more scones to bake.

Mrs. Roberts wanted her favorite table by the window for afternoon tea at three o'clock, two more reservations for our "Tea by the Sea" next weekend, one additional child for our end-of-summer cooking class, and Sally Stokes left a message that she would be dropping by. Just what I didn't want to hear!

People often have the misconception when you own a tea room that you have all the time in the world to walk around or sit down with guests and enjoy a pot of tea. The atmosphere and ambiance an owner creates makes guests so relaxed that

17

sometimes they don't realize all the work you do in creating this experience for them.

Today would be one of those days when I would be too busy to deal with Sally Stokes. I told myself to remember to tell the servers I was busy in the kitchen if she showed up.

And I would be! The Givens Princess tea party was now at twenty-five guests, and along with the other thirty-five guests we would be having for our one o'clock and three o'clock afternoon tea today, it was sure to be hectic. I was glad Sarah had offered to help me!

I quickly washed my hands, slipped on my black and white toile apron and began preparations to make a quadruple batch of chocolate chip scones at the birthday girl's request. Sure, there are plenty of scone mixes out there that many other tea rooms used, but nothing was as good as making them from scratch. Yes, it was time consuming, but worth it! I would miss this aspect of the tea room, almost more than the guests!

I enjoyed the quiet peacefulness of mornings to myself when the rest of the world was still sleeping in. Baking and cooking have always been therapeutic to me, and as I listened to my newest Yo Yo Ma cello C.D. I felt all the worries of yesterday lifted from my shoulders.

Standing at my kitchen window, I could see the bright red male cardinal sitting on the back fence singing. He was a regular at the bird feeder and I enjoyed the tenderness he displayed towards his mate as he actually fed bird seed into her beak.

Adding the herb garden and bird feeders to the back yard had been a wonderful addition to the tea room. I never got tired of the ever-changing view. Shane and Charlie had worked together to clear the space and get the bed ready for planting the herbs. The addition of the bird houses was a Mother's Day present from Emma and Charlie. The thought of leaving this behind made me sad. We would have to recreate this beautiful herb garden and bird haven outside my office window. I would have to have something beautiful to inspire me!

The phone rang as I found myself pulled out of my day dream. Who in the world would call at six thirty in the morning? I wiped the scone dough from my hands and grabbed the phone before the voice mail got it.

"Good Morning, The Pink Dogwood Tea Room," I cheerfully said. "How can I help you?"

"Hey, Amelia, it's Lacey," a sleepy voice said. "I am not feeling well this morning. I think I won't be in today."

Lacey was a college student who most likely had been out late again with her friends. This was the third time she had called in sick in the last month.

"Gee Lacey, again?" I asked sarcastically. If there's one thing I can't stand, it is irresponsible behavior! "This has become quite a habit. Maybe it's time you thought of moving on if your schedule at the tea room is interfering with your late night extracurricular activities," I told her.

I think my comment caught Lacey off-guard. She didn't quite have a response for me. "In fact Lacey, there are going to be some changes around here, so maybe this is for the best," I told her. Illness was understandable and sometimes people truly did need to stay home and in bed. I tried to be as understanding as possible. But three times in one month, especially on a busy Saturday? Lacey was aware of our hectic schedule.

"I'm sorry Mrs. Spencer. I let you down again. You're right," Lacey said. She didn't seem especially devastated.

"I appreciate your honesty, but Lacey, we are making some major changes. And I need people I can count on. Take some time to think about what I have said and call me when you know you are committed to your schedule," I said, my voice softening. Having these talks with the servers was not easy and the least enjoyable part of owning the tea room. But in my heart, I knew this was a wise decision.

"Okay, I will, Mrs. Spencer. Sorry." She said and hung up the phone.

All right, back to the bird show!

An hour later, the scones were baking, cream of tomato soup was simmering on the stove, and I was just finishing up sixty beautiful mini artichoke quiches, ready for the oven. Everything was running on time.

I did a quick sweep through the main dining room to see if everything was in order. The two downstairs bathrooms would need a quick cleaning. I hurriedly took off my apron, grabbed my caddy of cleaning supplies and headed to do the task.

Sarah was due to come in at any time along with Emily and Gretchen, both of whom had been working at The Pink Dogwood since we opened. What was nice about these two ladies was that they knew what to do without asking.

If the sugar cubes were low, they would refill the sugar bowls. If we were low on certain teas (we only had forty-five seasonal teas to keep track of at any given time) they filled out a low inventory alert form for me so I could fax it over to Shane. They made sure the beverage station was stocked, the glasses were filled with ice and kept frosty cold in the freezer, lemons were sliced, and creamers were filled with milk and in the refrigerator. It was like a tight run ship and had to be. Any detail that could be done ahead would save a lot of running time between the tables and the kitchen because one thing tea room guests demand is attention to detail.

We have learned over the years that many of our guests have certain preferences — preferences in tables, in rooms, and will make special requests ahead of time for certain favorite soups, quiches, desserts and teas. We try to please everyone. When you are in the tea room business, you are in the people-pleasing business!

I put my apron back on, ready to start setting the tables, something we usually do the day before, but we had so many guests on Friday that we didn't have extra table cloths at the end of the day. I was fluffing them in the dryer as I configured the reservations and seating times on a diagram.

"Good Morning!" Sarah chirped as she walked in. She hung her purse on the coat rack and looked for a freshly pressed toile half apron to put on. We have a uniform of white shirt, black pants and toile aprons. Hair is pulled back or up if long. Small earrings are appropriate along with black flat shoes, never clunky loud heels.

"Hey, Sarah! I am so glad you are here!"

Emily and Gretchen arrived soon after, and we all began dressing tables.

"Good morning ladies!" I said with a smile. "Put on your roller skates 'cause it's going to be a dilly of a day! Can y'all give me a hand setting up the dining rooms? Thanks!"

I never tire of looking at our beautiful Victorian from the curved staircase sweeping up the left side of the foyer to the largest of the dining rooms elaborately wallpapered in burgundy and hunter green. The "Pink Lady" is stunning! The green flooring tiles, tiffany stained glass chandeliers, green tiled fireplace and twelve foot ceilings draped with wall paper have left more than one guest oohing and ahhing.

My favorite space in the house is the powder room decorated with five different wall paper treatments and the feature attraction—the original one hundred six year old claw foot tub. More than one guest over the years has commented, "You've got to go in there and see that beautiful wall paper. Go wash your hands or something! Take a picture!"

Our smaller, more intimate dining room is off to the right of the foyer. Many guests have told me it is a favorite place for them to sit and visit with friends, decorated in soft pinks and blues. The room features a stained-glass mantle with a heart and tulip motif, and a soft pattern of birds and roses adorn the wall paper. It seats up to twelve quite comfortably at our antique tables.

This room originally served as the parlor in the home when it was built in 1904.

The gift shop is located straight through the foyer and is the center room of the downstairs. It also has a fireplace tiled in cobalt blue and is filled with our antiques for sale. This room was the original dining room in the house. We have our entire assortment of teas available for purchase along with tea pots, infusers, music, candles, gift baskets and our coffees from The Smoky Mountain Coffee Herb and Tea Company. Everything is carefully placed on Shane's antiques displayed throughout the tea room.

In case of unexpected walk-ins or party overflow, we also have two round antique tables by the windows overlooking the herb garden. It has been the perfect spot for someone wanting to come in and enjoy tea by themselves with a book or to sit and contemplate the birds. It's also the perfect spot to watch our porch kitty, Lily, curl up and take a nap out on the wicker love seat. She has such a fan club that we had to give her a blog on our website.

As we placed the last cup and saucer on the tables, the front door opened and our first reservation arrived. Sarah had an overview of the day's reservations and table assignments. She would greet and seat everyone and then help Emily handle the Givens Princess Party at eleven o'clock in the large burgundy dining room. Gretchen was in charge of the blue dining room reservations and overflow tables in the gift shop.

I headed back to the kitchen to get the quiche out of the oven and began setting up the three tiered tea trays for the Princess Party. The tea parties begin with each guest selecting her own pot of tea from our seasonal hot tea menu. After the tea has been poured, a tea cup of cream of tomato soup is placed at each guest's place setting.

Next, the servers take out a beautiful silver basket lined with a hand-embroidered napkin and filled with our warm scones.

Today's flavor of the day was chocolate chip. We serve our scones with my almond cream recipe and strawberry preserves or homemade lemon curd, worth the extra effort.

After the scones, it's time for the British style three-tiered tray. We are serving individual mini artichoke quiches this afternoon, along with cucumber and herb cream cheese tea sandwiches and a mini turkey cranberry grilled Panini as the savory layer.

The dessert tier was sure to be a hit. Key lime truffles rolled in toasted coconut, chocolate dipped strawberries, and miniature triple chocolate bliss Bundt cakes. Of course, we always served one grand finale dessert. Today's selection was a triple berry English trifle with lemon sponge cake. It was worth every calorie and fat gram.

Sarah and Emily handled the Givens party with ease. It was sweet seeing all the girls dressed as their favorite princesses. I managed to step out of the kitchen for a while and greet the girls and their Moms. Clean up was always a project after these affairs, but they were always enjoyable parties for us to host.

Gretchen handled the gift shop and stepped in to oversee and help with the clean up and transition of the burgundy room for afternoon tea. We chased a few pink boa feathers and sequins around, changed table cloths, reset the tables and swept the floors. We were ready for the big crowd!

I had already started preparing the tea trays for the reservations we had on the books. I always made additional sweets and savories just in case we had a walk-in unfamiliar with our reservation policy. I had learned over the years that is was far easier to do business by "reservation only" to conserve on groceries, to prevent waste and to always keep our regular guests coming back. They appreciated the time and attention it took to prepare their table and tea tray.

The one o'clock afternoon tea reservations began drifting in slowly. Some ladies enjoyed the hunt for treasure in the gift shop and spent time looking before they were ready to be seated.

Others wanted to try a new tea selection. We happened to have a wonderful new chocolate mint tea that had just arrived in yesterday's tea shipment. It smelled like a refreshing peppermint patty. Several pots had been ordered already this afternoon.

"Things are going well," Sarah told me as she breezed through the kitchen. "We have had to make several pitchers of your signature peach iced tea today because of the heat wave."

"Thanks for coming in this morning!" I sincerely said. I filled her in about Lacey and she shook her head sadly.

"If I had a job like this, you couldn't keep me away! I love working at the library, but we are open seven days a week and have evening hours also. Sometimes I wish I could set my own schedule," she told me.

"You definitely set your own schedule when you run a tea room," I said and laughed. "It's usually much longer hours than a regular job. Emma complains that if she wants to spend time with her mother, she has to come by the tea room. But, there are fringe benefits for her such as having her friends over anytime for tea and we always have something wonderful for her to eat after school," I elaborated.

"My idea of a childhood dream come true," Sarah said wistfully.

"Would you be interested in filling in when your library schedule allows?" I asked Sarah hopefully.

She paused and set her tray on the counter. She began twirling her hair, something she does when she is in deep thought.

"I want to talk with you and Shane about something," she started to say, when all the sudden, Sally Stokes burst into the kitchen.

"Hello, hello, ladies and Miss Amelia!" Sally said waving her hands in the air resembling a flapping bird. "How are y'all doing this beautiful day?"

How she had managed to get past my pit bulls, I wondered? I had left strict orders to keep her away from me. Plus I had signs posted at the entrance to the kitchen door that plainly stated, "Employees Only Past This Point."

"Hey, Sally!" I said attempting to be civil. I got your message. We're awfully busy today and in the middle of our afternoon tea rush. Can I call you when it's a better time?" I strongly hinted.

"This won't take too long, pinky promise," she shrilled in her high pitched twang, extending her pinkie in the air.

She was going to be harder to get rid of than bed bugs! Boy this woman was persistent!

"What can I do for you?" I asked quite abruptly. Sarah raised her eyebrows with a look of surprise on her face.

"I heard from a certain someone," she exclaimed, "that y'all were selling The Pink Dogwood!" She placed her hands on her ample hips and continued, "And I said, 'Well no one told me!' So here I am, ready with paper work to list this house." She took out a packet of papers from her tote bag and slapped them down on the counter.

"When do you want to have your open house? Is next weekend a good time?" she smiled, oblivious to everyone around her.

"No, next week is not a good time!" I snapped. I stepped back from the counter and approached her. "Who told you we were selling The Pink Dogwood?" I asked.

"Oh, you know, I will never tell. A little birdie whispered in my ear," she whispered as she giggled, and her body shook like Jello.

I was getting hot under the collar. I didn't like to be put on the spot and Sally was doing just that! My laid-back personality was being tested.

Sarah quickly exited the kitchen taking care of the guests who were ready to be seated for afternoon tea. Sarah and I would have to continue our conversation later.

"Sally, you're going to have to forgive me, but I have tea trays to complete, and this really isn't a good time for me," I said, my face flushing crimson. I hoped she took the hint.

"That's okay, Sugar. I can just wait back here in the kitchen and have a tall glass of your peach iced tea and wait 'til everyone is gone!" she said.

"Oh, no!" I exclaimed, wondering how much firmer I would have to be with her. "We will be here for hours. Besides, I will have to talk with Shane before I can fill out any kind of paper work."

"Oh, you have one of those marriages where you have to run everything by the man of the house, right?" she said playing devil's advocate, glancing at my facial expression from the corner of her eyes.

This woman was pushing it!

"Sarah! Can you help Ms. Stokes out?" I yelled with forced happiness in my voice form the kitchen, hoping to catch Sarah's attention. I turned towards Sally with a plastered Cheshire grin on my face.

"It's been real nice, Amelia," Sally murmured as she sashayed out the kitchen door way. "Call me!"

It would be a cold day in H-E-Double L hockey sticks, I thought to myself. I was going to ask Shane who leaked out our information!

Chapter Three

After picking up Emma and her friend Julia from the mall, I directed "Lady Bug" to head home. I wanted to speak to Shane to find out how Sally had heard our news so quickly.

"Mom! You just ran a red light!" Emma squealed from the back seat. "Are you okay?" Her blue eyes were as large as saucers.

"Oh my word!" I exclaimed, slowing "Lady Bug" down to the legal speed limit. "All I need is a ticket. I am sorry girls. I seem to be distracted this afternoon." I decided to slow down and focus on getting home safely and without a run in with the law. In small towns, especially towards the end of the month, it seems the police set up a lot of speed traps to meet their monthly quota. I was lucky this time.

"Are you okay, Mrs. Spencer?" Julia asked. I think she was relieved we were almost to her home and to safety.

"I am fine, girls. Just business stuff!" I reassured them and tried to force a smile. I was still fuming from my visit with Sally.

After depositing Julia safely at home, I drove the three miles to our home under the speed limit and pulled "Lady Bug" into the garage. Shane stood at the garage door with Charlie who was covered in mud and grass stains from football practice.

"Hey Mom!" Charlie called out as we got out of the car. "I threw three touch downs." He was sweaty with streaks of dirt on his face. He was definitely transitioning from little boy to young man, his once little boy round face thinning and his shoulders becoming much broader.

"Wow! That's excellent, Charlie!" I said. I was so proud of how hard he was focusing on school and his sports. "I can't wait for your first game. It's going to be your year!"

Shane tousled Charlie's hair and patted his back, beaming with pride. Charlie was Shane made over complete with freckles across the bridge of his nose. It was hard to tell Shane's school pictures from Charlie's except for Shane's 1970s big lapel shirt collars.

"Hey, bud. Why don't you head to the shower and I will get dinner ready," I suggested to Charlie. "And don't forget to scrub with your washcloth behind your ears this time," I reminded him. He quickly ran inside. There was one thing Charlie didn't miss and that was a meal! Reminding him to wash behind his ears was still somewhat necessary.

"Emma, honey," I turned and spoke to her. "Could you go ahead and set the table for dinner? I need to speak to your Dad for a minute in private."

"Sure, Mom," She said. She was turning out to be such a responsible young lady. I was actually enjoying the teen years so far!

Shane turned to me with worry on his face.

"What's wrong, babe?" he asked. "Did something happen at work today?"

"Well, I guess you could say that," I told him. "Let's head out to the porch and I will fill you in."

I walked through our cozy kitchen and inhaled the aroma of pot roast wafting through the house. Crock pots are a wonderful invention. Though I cook all day long at The Pink Dogwood, I don't always make it home in time to cook a homemade meal. It's like the cobbler's family who never had nice shoes. The crock pot made life easier for me.

I walked over to my kitchen desk area where our mail basket was and glanced down at today's mail. I picked up the stack and carried it outside with me and plopped down in my favorite wicker chair. I placed the stack of mail in my lap and took a sideways glance at Shane.

I loved sitting on the porch. This time of the evening was when the birds visited the feeders and the temperature cooled off to a more tolerable level. Shane and I always seemed to share our most important news of the day and decision making out here. It was a wonderful extension of our living space.

"Enough suspense already," Shane said. "What is going on?"

"Did you call Sally Stokes and tell her we were selling 'The Pink Lady?'" I asked him looking him straight in the eyes.

"Why would I do that after all the stress she caused us when we dealt with her before?" Shane said with a quizzical look on his face. "Why would you even think I would do that?"

I shared with him Sally's surprise visit to the kitchen and described our conversation to him. He seemed shocked.

"Look, I don't know how she found out. I do have something to tell you, though," he said and paused. He looked serious. Shane is usually happy go lucky, so I knew this was important.

"I have a buyer for The Pink Dogwood," he told me matter-of-factly.

"A buyer, already?" I exclaimed. "I haven't even had time to process the fact that we are selling, yet." Was my head spinning or was it just my imagination?

"Dawson Interiors wants to buy the building," Shane said. He reached for my hand and began rubbing my arm. "They want to move a satellite location down town."

"Dawson Interiors? Aren't they the firm with an office in Nashville?" I asked Shane. Jake White had done a nice write up on Dawson Interiors recently in *The Dogwood Daily*. They were sponsoring a room in the Dogwood Cove Symphony Showcase House at Cassandra's request.

"Yes. They approached me a few months back and asked if we were interested in selling," Shane said and continued stroking my arm as if he were putting me in a trance.

"You never mentioned that to me. Why not?" I asked him. I sat up straight as the induced trance began to subside.

"Well, when they approached me, it was not the right time. We weren't ready to sell," he explained. "So, I didn't bother mentioning it."

"Didn't bother mentioning it?" I asked him. "How could you *not* mention something that important? It's just our business and livelihood!" Though I trusted Shane with most business decisions, this was an oversight that surprised me.

"You were under a tremendous amount of stress getting ready for that photo shoot for *Southern Living Magazine*. Remember how you were barely sleeping?" he gently reminded me. "I didn't want to add to your stress when it obviously wasn't the right time to even consider selling the tea room."

I remembered that week. I was a nervous wreck and uncharacteristically snappy with everyone! Cleaning from floor to ceiling, perfecting my tea tray for the photographer and getting the gardens ready was a tremendous undertaking.

The article had turned out well and resulted in a beautiful story about Dogwood Cove and "The Pink Lady." We saw a real boost in tourism in Dogwood Cove after we appeared in the magazine.

"Oh, yeah!" I said and remembered, shaking my head. "That was a very stressful time. No wonder why you didn't bring it up. I could hardly eat that week! I think I was on the verge of an ulcer."

"Well, Dawson Interiors has made a very substantial offer and one we really can't turn down. It's three times what we paid for house," he said.

"Three times?" I was shocked. "That's great! I never expected we would get that much. Are they planning on running The Pink Dogwood downstairs and housing their offices upstairs?"

30

Shane's face said it all. I didn't want to hear what came next. "No, sweetie! There will not be a tea room downstairs," he said as he looked at me with concern on his face.

I sat back and my mouth fell open. I didn't know what to say, what to think, and suddenly, I was filled with an overwhelming sadness. No tea room! It was finally settling in. There would be no Pink Dogwood Tea Room. No little girl "Princess Tea Parties," no more tea tasting classes, no place special to celebrate those important milestones such as baby showers and bridal showers. This was going to be a blow to Dogwood Cove. I felt like I had just lost my best friend.

"I don't feel good about this, Shane," I said and shook my head, as the realization sank in. "This is going to be devastating for a lot of ladies in town. When we talked about selling The Pink Dogwood, we talked about selling the business and training the new owners. I guess I assumed it would stay a tea room," I continued. My voice had become quivery, and I felt the tears burning my eyes.

Shane knew that The Pink Dogwood was an extension of me. I had put my heart, soul, and sweat equity into building it into a business that had quite a following. Visit any tea room and find that each one is as unique as the person who runs it. A tea room is truly a reflection of the owner's style and personality.

"Amelia, I know you are upset, but I don't think we will ever get an offer this generous," Shane said, dabbing my eyes with a tissue. "Remember, you are still going to be active in the tea business with Smoky Mountain Coffee, Herb and Tea Company! Think of how far ahead we will be with such a substantial offer."

Yeah—Shane had moved on. He was far more practical than I, and he was able to view business as business. I, on the other hand, was far more emotional about The Pink Dogwood. I couldn't imagine there not being a tea room for all Dogwood Cove's celebrations!

In the past, Shane had joked with me that I reminded him of Meg Ryan's character, Kathleen Kelly, in *You've Got Mail*. She owned a little bookstore called *The Shop Around The Corner*. When Tom Hanks' character, Joe Fox, opened his large chain bookstore, *Fox Books*, and began winning over customers, he told Kathleen, "It's not personal. It's just business." She replied, "Well, it's not just business to me. It's personal!" That's how I often felt about the tea room.

I glanced down at the pile of mail still sitting in my lap now covered with big splats of tears. There was an envelope on top with a running mustang logo on it. I wondered what fundraiser needed my attention. I was still crying, but tore into the mail. Anything to keep my mind temporarily preoccupied.

"What's that?" Shane asked.

I opened the letter from my Alma Mater, Southern Methodist University, a liberal arts college nestled in the Highland Park area of Dallas, Texas. It was a small college of about six thousand undergraduate students with a strong law, business and graduate programs.

"Oh, as if my day couldn't be any more special, I just got a reminder that I am getting older! Check me for grey hair," I sighed; "It's an invitation to homecoming and my twenty-year college class reunion."

"Old SMU," Shane said. "That sounds like fun!"

I had taken the family for a weekend visit several years ago. The campus reminded me of one of those old fashioned hollow Easter eggs made of sugar. Peek inside and see a beautiful spring scene, so beautiful, one hated to eat it! I always thought the way the oak trees lined the entrance of the campus with Dallas Hall in the distance was like a glimpse of a perfect setting like the inside of one of those sugar Easter eggs.

The Georgian style architecture, brick paved walkways and immaculate landscaping gave the school a very Ivy League feel. I could still remember the day I took my first campus tour when

I was only eighteen years old. Back then I wore my hair in an 80s-inspired permed poof reminiscent of a *White Snake* video. During the tour, I remember being in awe of the architecture, the perfectly manicured lawns, and the fountain in the center of campus. But that was a long time ago and right now I didn't feel like being reminded of how just how long ago!

"I think I will put this into the shredder and be done with it," I told Shane. I started to get up from my wicker chair, invitation in hand.

"Hold on, Amelia," he said as he held up his hand. "I think it would do you good to have a change of scenery with all this tea room decision making going on now. A weekend on campus sounds good to me," he smiled brightly, oblivious to my dark mood which was quickly getting darker.

"I am not so sure I share your sentiments just right now. In fact, I would like to eat dinner and go soak in the tub and just not think about anything right now," I told him.

He knew we would discuss this another time. A good soak in our antique deep claw-foot tub could change any mood. I would just add a couple scoops of our aromatherapy line of green tea soaking salts with chamomile, lavender and peppermint and all my troubles and worries would be forgotten. Light a jasmine white tea candle, grab my favorite book and I would be set for relaxation! It was just what I needed.

"Why don't you get that bath started, Amelia sweetheart," Shane said. "I will keep your dinner warm and I will go ahead and eat with the kids tonight. You need some time for yourself."

Gosh, I loved that man! He knew when I needed my space and when I needed time to think. I decided to take him up on his generous offer.

"You know, you just reminded me why you are the world's greatest husband!" I said. I smiled and quickly kissed him.

"I plan on collecting from you later!" He lifted his eyebrow and gave me his trademark sexy look. Yes, one date with Shane and I knew he was the one. He understood me better than anyone else.

We walked back into the kitchen and Shane told Emma and Charlie to set the table for three. Mom would be temporarily detained.

I ran upstairs and started running the water. A good forty-five minutes later and I was a new woman. All the tension was gone from my neck and shoulders, all the stress was erased from my face, and the world was a much better place! I slipped on my favorite pajamas and fuzzy slippers and came downstairs to eat dinner.

Shane was just washing up the dinner dishes and had the dish towel draped over his shoulder.

"Here you go, sweetie!" He said as he placed a hot plate of pot roast and a salad in front of me. "The kids are upstairs finishing their homework. Do you want balsamic vinaigrette on your salad?"

"Hello!" I heard called out from the foyer. "Anyone home?"

"That sounds like Cassandra," I told Shane. "Cassandra? Is that you?" I called out getting up from the table.

"Yes, darlin' it is moi!" she sang out as she slid into the kitchen. "Sit down and eat. Don't let me interrupt your dinner."

"I called Cassandra while you were in the tub," Shane said. "Can I get you anything to drink or eat, Cassandra?"

"Oh, no honey!" She smiled. "Unless you happen to have some of Amelia's peach iced tea already made up."

"Coming right up!" he said and began filling a glass with ice. He looked over his shoulder to check my facial expression.

"What did you call Cassandra about, Shane?" I asked him wondering what these two had up their sleeves.

"Don't be upset with Shane, Amelia." Cassandra said as she patted my arm. "He thought you were having a hard day and needed some cheering up. So, here I am!"

Cassandra had a way of making everyone around her smile. Her personality was magnetic. She was a big flirt and loved to tease. It was hard to be down with her around. She was very generous with her time and had been a good friend to me over the years.

I took a bite of the pot roast and shook my head, smiling. "You are a sight for sore eyes tonight!" I told her. "I've really had a trying day."

I shared with her Sally Stokes visit to the tea room, Shane's news about Dawson Interiors and the fact that I was reminded how old I was getting with my college homecoming invitation arriving today.

"Southern Methodist was your college, right?" Cassandra asked.

"Go Mustangs!" Shane piped in bringing hot rolls and butter to the table. Cassandra helped herself and took a big bite.

"Sounds like a plan," she said, licking butter from her thumb.

"What plan?" I asked her not understanding what she was thinking.

"Well, I have a friend who owns the Adolphus Hotel in Dallas, and I am sure we could stay at the Presidential Suite and have a girl's weekend. What do you think?" She finished her roll and looked over at me.

"Sounds crazy! You're just as bad as he is," I told her and nodded my head in Shane's direction. "The last thing I need right now is a trip down memory lane. There are some things better left back in the past."

"Are you talking about your old boyfriend, Jett?" Shane asked. Did I detect a hint of jealously in his voice? He turned away from the sink and faced the table.

"Heavens no!" I reassured him. "I haven't heard from Jett since we got the invitation to his wedding ten years ago." Jett had been my college boyfriend and for a brief period, we were engaged. Leaving for London my senior year was perfect timing. I immersed myself in the culture, studied hard and traveled. Being abroad had allowed me time to heal. As soon as I returned from

London and graduated, I returned to Dogwood Cove. I always wondered why Jett had sent me a wedding invitation after the way things were left between us.

"I was thinking about Katherine," I told Shane.

"Have I missed something here?" Cassandra asked. "Who is this Katherine person?" She took a quick sip of peach iced tea and set her glass down giving me her full attention.

"Look, I loved SMU. I loved going away to college, and I loved Dallas. I just happened to get placed with a roommate who didn't work out so well."

That was the understatement of the century. Katherine and I were polar opposites. She was from the big city of Houston. She was very fashion forward and very sexy, which made her very popular with the guys on campus and she just happened to be a theatre major. She had a booming voice and a theatrical presence about her that demanded attention from everyone at all times. If she entered a room, her Giorgio Red Door perfume enveloped everything in its path. Everyone couldn't help but notice the way she sashayed across the room.

I was very different from Katherine. Coming from a small town, I had small-town values. I kept up with the fashion trends, but I chose to dress a bit more modestly than my roommate. I was shy and on the quiet side, but I loved meeting new people. I trusted people, maybe a bit too much, and I learned a lot of life lessons in the process. I guess one could say when I left Dogwood Cove I was a bit naive. Katherine had sensed that and taken advantage of my trusting nature.

"Well, sweetheart, Katherine Gold probably won't even be at the reunion," Shane said.

Shane is a lot like me. Did he actually think she would miss an opportunity to be the center of attention?

"Shane, she was our homecoming queen. Former homecoming queens always come back so they can be presented during the half-time show," I reminded him.

"This isn't the same Katherine Gold who is on a soap opera?" Cassandra said snapping her fingers, trying to remember. "Didn't she get voted best body in the soap industry?"

"Yep—one in the same!" I suddenly didn't feel like eating any more of my pot roast.

"I didn't know you were her roommate! Why didn't you tell me?" she asked excitedly.

"Well, it's something I try to forget about!" I told her. "I wouldn't exactly put it on my top ten list of things people should know about me." I shook my head at Shane and saw the supportive look in his eyes. He and I had started dating shortly after I graduated from SMU. He understood my lack of desire in discussing my past roommate with Cassandra.

"I think Amelia is hesitant to talk much about it because rooming with Katherine ended up being a nightmarish situation for her," Shane told Cassandra. "She is nothing like the character she plays on television."

Many people assumed that Katherine was just like Lindsey Tanner, who was the central character on the long running soap opera "The Rich and the Lost." Lindsey was adored by everyone and exhibited kindness, love and loyalty, a strict departure from who Katherine was in real life.

"So, Katherine Gold is actually a real witch!" Cassandra shouted. "I have heard a few stories about her out in L.A., but I never listen to half the stuff people gossip about out there," she informed us.

Cassandra should know with her "A List" friends she heard and saw a lot first hand. She was familiar with how different life was in Hollywood.

"Well, I don't like to call her a witch," I started to say when Shane interrupted.

"She is and was to you and I don't mind being the one to say that she's a witch," Shane said.

Shane doesn't get easily rattled, but he knew the pain I had experienced because of Katherine. He was not going to let her off the hook for that!

"I still think Dallas would be the perfect girls' getaway and what better excuse than a homecoming football weekend!" Cassandra chirped, full of enthusiasm and high spirits. "I doubt we will even run into this Katherine Gold person, so don't let that keep you from going. She'll probably be busy getting a mini-lift or a tummy tuck." She was having fun with this!

"Cassandra has a point, Amelia," Shane said. "You could use a fun weekend with the girls. I can hold down the fort here and the kids and I could plan a camping trip." He never ceased to surprise me. He was continually my rock.

"Let me think about it, okay?" I said looking at both of them. "I'm going to have a lot on my plate with packing up The Pink Dogwood, scheduling movers and, of course, I will want to have one final tea party for all my guests from over the years."

"When's the reunion?" Cassandra asked.

"It's five weeks from today. It's the big Rice game," I told her.

Rice was one of our biggest rivals when SMU played in the now defunct South Western Conference. We played all of our games at Texas Stadium where the Dallas Cowboys had played. Texas Stadium was a good 45 minute drive from our campus. Now the football games were held on campus at the new Gerald J. Ford Stadium completed in the year 2000. Some of our more famous Alumni included golfer Payne Stewart, First Lady Laura Bush, actress Kathy Bates, Heisman Trophy winner Doak Walker and legendary television producer Aaron Spelling.

I had not been back for a football game since my freshmen year when our football program received the death penalty for recruiting violations, a blow that would have devastating effects for years on the school. We went from posh games at Texas Stadium to no games, no practices and no recruiting for several years. My senior year, we were allowed to have a football team again, the difference being that the players were required to pass the same stringent enrollment qualifications that every other student had to go through to be accepted at SMU.

I actually had to admit to myself that I was excited to attend a game at the new stadium that seated up to thirty-two thousand spectators. It would be nice to be in the middle of all the homecoming festivities and see the campus draped in red and blue, our school colors. And a weekend with Olivia, Cassandra and Sarah was just what I needed to get my mind off the sale of the tea room.

"I will let Albert know that he will be flying us in the corporate jet five weeks from now and I will go ahead and book the Adolphus Presidential Suite for that weekend," Cassandra said smiling with confidence. "Be prepared to shop because Neiman Marcus is right down the street from the Adolphus," she continued.

Now this was sounding good! I couldn't remember the last time I had stepped foot inside a Neiman Marcus, but I always enjoyed the fantastic store displays that made Neiman's so legendary.

"I will consent to the trip if you allow me to take everyone for afternoon tea at the Adolphus. They have a wonderful French tea salon, my treat!" I told Cassandra, while a big smile spread across my face.

"You're on," she said. I could feel all the stress from talking about Katherine Gold dissipating. I was beginning to look forward to our weekend in Dallas.

Chapter Four

The next few weeks flew by at a record pace. With the start of a new school year and preparing for the sale of The Pink Dogwood, I had every moment of the day filled.

Emma had band practice every day after school until six o'clock in the evening. Her game and competition schedule kept the weekends tied up. Charlie had foot ball practice three times a week and games on Saturday afternoons. I did my best to be at all band performances and football games. It was important to me to be supportive of my children.

Shane met with Dawson Interiors and began drawing up the real estate contract. If everything went according to plan, we should close on the tea room a week after we got back from Dallas. I decided to keep the tea room open until the last day. I would do the bulk of my packing after our weekend in Dallas.

As word spread throughout Dogwood Cove about the sale of the tea room along with a nice write up by Jake White in *The Dogwood Daily*, reservations began pouring in from everywhere. Our guests wanted to make sure they had an opportunity to have one last afternoon tea with us and I was committed to making sure it would be spectacular.

I think being so busy kept me from having any more crying spells. I came close a few times when some of our regular guests began pulling tissues out of their purses and remarking how sad-

dened they were that they no longer would have a place so wonderful to celebrate their special occasions. I felt the same way,
but I pushed on and reminded myself that this was what we had
planned for and tried to look at the bigger picture.

Emma and Charlie had mixed feelings about the sale. They
were excited that I would have more free time to spend with
them and not have every Saturday tied up. But on the other
hand, they had grown up in the tea room and participated in all
of our children's tea parties, cooking and etiquette classes and
had entertained their friends there over the years. I assured them
that I would still have all my homemade goodies. They could just
enjoy them at home instead of at the tea room.

Sarah was a big help working with me whenever she had a
free day from her library schedule. With all the extra reservations, we really needed the help!

"Gosh, I am going to miss being here!" she told me one afternoon. "What are you going to do with Lily? Will she be moving
out to your home?" Sarah asked. Lily! I had not even thought
about what we were going to do with the cat. She loved watching the birds from her chair on the porch.

"I guess she will move to our place, though I hate to think
of how much she will miss being here. It's as if she goes with the
house," I told Sarah.

Lily had adopted us when she was three weeks old. I was
making a batch of scones when I heard a terrible commotion
coming from the house next door. I walked outside and saw this
little tiny kitten hissing at two large dogs inside a chain length
fence. I scooped her up as she was still spitting with her tail
puffed up, and brought her to our porch. I soon realized she was
starving and opened a can of tuna for her. She had been with us
ever since.

Her amber eyes and beautiful gray, black and gold stripes
made her an attraction at the tea room. Her antics, such as
chasing after snowflakes and fighting snakes in our herb garden,

made for wonderful stories on our webpage, and we soon added Lily's blog to keep our guests updated on her latest adventures. Lily was as much a part of the tea room as I was, and I wasn't sure she would appreciate being separated from her porch.

Sarah had brought up a very important issue that I had not even thought of — Lily. Sarah had impressed me with how thoughtful she was about so many aspects of the tea room. She made me wish I had invited her to work with me much earlier. I was glad that both Sarah and Olivia would be coming for the weekend to Dallas.

"Are you finished packing for Big D?" I asked Sarah while we were setting tables a few days before we flew out.

"I am not quite sure what to pack," she said. "I know there is a cocktail reception Friday evening, the homecoming parade, BBQ and an early Saturday game. Am I forgetting something?" she asked.

"Don't forget comfortable shoes for shopping at North Park Mall and I hope we get to go dancing in Ft. Worth so Olivia will be happy to mingle with some real cowboys," I said as I threw back my head and laughed.

"Well, I will have to pack my ostrich boots for that night. I've got the perfect outfit in mind for some 'boot scootin boogie!'" she giggled.

I didn't know how we were going to fit so many activities in such a short trip, but we always managed to do a lot whenever "The Traveling Tea Ladies" got together. This trip would be no exception.

"I am glad the library agreed to let you have some time off," I told Sarah.

"Well, I do have seniority there since I have worked there so many years," she said with a wistful look in her eyes.

Sarah had seemed much more contemplative than usual. Maybe it was because we were spending more time together lately and I was noticing it more, but something didn't seem quite right.

"Sarah, are you doing okay these days?" I asked her, the concern evident in my voice. "I couldn't help but notice you have seemed like you have something on your mind these days," I continued.

She stepped back and crossed her arms. She looked up at me and seemed surprised I had noticed.

"I am okay. I just have been thinking about a lot of things," she stated.

"Is it about Jake?" I inquired.

I thought maybe she and Jake had reconsidered and tried to work things out. They seemed to complement each other so well.

"He's part of it. We've been talking lately, but for now, we are keeping it strictly platonic. Actually, it's my fault. I just feel so restless. I don't feel like I am getting anywhere at the library."

This was not what I expected to hear from her. She had been at Dogwood Cove Library since she was in high school and began volunteering on the weekends. She had gone to the University of Tennessee, earned her degree and applied for the children's librarian position. She had been there for eight years now.

"Are you waiting on a promotion?" I asked. I hadn't heard her say anything about applying for a promotion.

"No. It's not about a promotion or a raise," she said as she shrugged her shoulders and continued to explain. "I just don't feel creatively challenged anymore. I need more!" she announced.

Creatively challenged. Sarah needed to express her creativity. Her wardrobe was evidence of that. I was sure she had some costumes planned for the weekend. Feeling stifled and underutilized was what she was battling.

"Don't get me wrong, Amelia," she pleaded. "I love the children and I love the people I work with. It's all I have been doing for the past eight years and I need a change. I don't know how else to explain it," she said exasperated.

I understood how she felt. I had taken a risk when I left my steady paycheck to begin The Pink Dogwood Tea Room. I was tired of making my boss look good and building his business. He was more than thrilled to have me on his "dream team," but it wasn't my dream. It was only after Shane's urging that I decided to pursue my tea education, and it had paid off.

I do understand what you mean," I reassured her and gave her a hug. "I have actually been in your shoes. It sounds like you are contemplating a change," I continued.

"Yes. I just don't know what yet, but I am hoping to figure some of that out while we are in Dallas," she said with a hopeful smile.

"You've been a good friend to me over the years, Sarah. If I can be of help, I am here for you."

"Thanks, Amelia!" she brightened. "Working with you on and off the past few weeks has really been fun for me. I feel like I've been able to see the other side of running the tea room and I really have enjoyed it," Sarah smiled and squeezed my hand.

"Hey, let's make a pot of tea and sit down and talk some more," I suggested. "Which tea would you like today? Jasmine, apricot or genmaicha? You choose."

"I would like to try the Japanese genmaicha today. It smells like a rice cake and I love that is a green tea and has so many health benefits," Sarah added. "All the polyphenols and antioxidants found in green tea have convinced me to drink at least four cups daily. I feel like I'm doing something good for my body!"

"Well, you are and I think this tea is so interesting with its kernels of fried rice and popcorn. It has been a best seller with our online customers," I told her.

"I can see why," Sarah said as she inhaled the aroma of the steeping tea. "I can't wait to try it," she said and brought the cup to her lips.

And she wasn't disappointed. It was the perfect pot of tea for two friends sharing their dreams, aspirations, and hopes for the future. Sarah had integrity and was trustworthy, something I hold in the highest esteem.

"We need to do this more often," I told her. "Sometimes it's just hard for me to stop and take time for tea. Maybe I will be forced to do that more often with Smoky Mountain Coffee, Herb and Tea Company since I will have to do so much taste testing and blending myself. One of the perks of the business!" I said excited.

"Yeah, what about your tea tasting classes? Are you still going to teach those?" Sarah asked.

"I haven't figured that out yet, but I still would like to have classes on a regular basis. That would allow me to keep in touch with so many of my regular guests. I will just have to find a venue to host the tea tastings," I shared with her.

We finished up our tea, I fed Lily and headed out to run errands and finish packing for the trip. My first stop was to pick up Emma at Riverbend Farm. She was volunteering with the therapeutic riding classes today.

"Hey, Olivia!" I called out as I parked "Lady Bug."

Olivia was unloading a wagon full of hay bales. She was swinging bales from the flat bed of the wagon into the hay loft where one of her farm hands was waiting to stack them. She handled the heavy bales as if they were as light as a bag of trash. She never ceased to amaze me.

"Hey, there Amelia!" she called to me, wiping sweat from her brow with her forearm. "It sure is a hot one today!"

Even though it was October, the days were still quite warm. I loved the crisp fall mornings in Dogwood Cove and the way the skies were that brilliant sapphire blue that only occur in autumn. It was my favorite time of year!

"If you think it's hot here, wait until we get to Dallas. I hope you packed light weight clothes for the trip," I said.

"I haven't even packed yet. I'm just going to throw some jeans and a couple of outfits together," Olivia admitted.

That was typical Olivia. Carefree, not concerned with fashion. She just packed jeans and something comfortable. She always managed to look beautiful whatever she wore. Her red hair was the envy of many.

"Liv. You're forgetting the cocktail party. Do you have a black dress?" I asked.

"I was thinking more of a dressy pant suit. Don't worry, I won't let you down," she assured me.

I should have guessed pant suit. She would look fantastic.

"David, I am taking a break for a minute," she called to the farm hand in the hay loft.

"Let's have something cold to drink and go inside for a minute," Olivia said.

"Good idea, Olivia!" I agreed.

I loved her kitchen with its arched stone fireplace. It was such a cozy addition to the ranch house. It was the perfect place to share conversation and look out at the river below.

"What would you like, a soft drink, water, or lemonade iced tea?" she asked.

"Oh, the lemonade iced tea sounds perfect! Thank you!" I enthused. And it was! Cold, slightly sweet and tart at the same time.

"Cassandra told me about this Katherine Gold woman, Amelia. What's the story on her?" Olivia finally asked.

I cleared my throat and paused a moment. I took another sip of tea before I began speaking.

"Remember I dated someone at SMU?" I said, not knowing quite what to say next.

"Dated? I thought you were engaged. What was his name, Jeff? Jed?" Olivia asked.

"Jett. Jett Rollins," I responded flatly. This was becoming hard for me.

"Yeah, I guess we were all surprised when you came home after graduation. I guess it worked out for the best, since you met Shane after that," Olivia stated.

Thank the Lord for blessings. Little did I know at the time that I was being led to my soul mate and that sometimes bad things happen for a reason.

"Yes, Jett and I were engaged . . . briefly, very briefly." I added.

"What was that all about?" Olivia asked point blank and refilled our tea glasses.

"Well, I sort of found him in a compromising situation with another woman," I said and nodded my head and took a deep breath. "It was Katherine Gold, my roommate," I added.

"She IS a witch! I tell you what I would have done. I would have taken her by the hair and tossed her out the door!" Olivia yelled with emphasis and made quick repetitive circles above her head as if she was spinning an invisible lasso.

That was Olivia. She was brutally honest and easily hurt.

I started laughing at the visual image of Katherine being tossed around by her hair. At the time that might have been a knee jerk reaction, but I didn't go there. I was never one to get into the gutter and fight. Some may see that as a weakness. I chose to see it as not compromising my values.

"What did you do?" she asked.

"I simply shut the door and never spoke to either one of them again. I was due to fly out the next day to London," I said. That had been a very painful day for me and one I tried hard to block from my memory.

But the pain gradually subsided and after graduation, I returned to Dogwood Cove and got busy. Shane had returned home from his summer abroad in Europe, back-packing and staying at youth hostels. He happened to be in town visiting his Aunt Alice. We ran into each other at a downtown Friday night music festival in nearby historic Jonesborough, Tennessee and soon became inseparable.

The one thing he had to be patient with me about was trust. After what Jett and Katherine had done, it was going to take me a while. He had graduate school to get back to, so we began a long distance courtship. When I shared with him what had happened, he became angry.

"Why would anyone in their right mind let you go?" he asked incredulously.

I responded, "Have you seen Katherine Gold on television?" By then she had started on "The Rich and the Lost." "She's gorgeous and got voted one of *People's Magazine* '100 Most Beautiful People.'"

"And?" he asked, obviously not impressed.

"And she's a knock out!" I told him.

"And have you looked in the mirror? Amelia, you are beautiful at so many different levels. I love your beautiful blue eyes, your bright smile, they way you light up a room, but most of all I love who you are and your honesty and the fact that you are not complicated. There are not a lot of women like you!" Shane said emphatically.

I blushed at his complements. What was his angle?, I wondered.

He saw the look on my face and knew he had not convinced me.

"I am going to marry you, Amelia. You are everything I have ever wanted," he said and took my hands in his. "I don't know what this Jett guy's problem was, but I'm glad he let you go. His mistake is my gain," Shane reassured me.

Fifteen years later, I have no regrets and two beautiful children. Shane and I were happy.

"You have a lot more control than I do," Olivia said. "I'm not sure I would have just walked out without at least telling him he was a dog."

"I haven't spoken to either of them since. I did get an invitation to Jett's wedding and I hear he married well. I'm happy for him," I told her.

"I wouldn't be so generous, I'm afraid," Olivia spoke truthfully.

"I look at it as I'm glad I found out before I married him. I would have been devastated if that happened after we married. It was a blessing," I said with conviction.

"Did Katherine ever marry?" Olivia asked.

I quickly responded, "No, and from what the tabloids say, she is dating some 'boy toy' thirteen years her junior. I don't think she will ever settle down and marry someone. I think she simply wanted to take Jett away from me. He was a challenge to her."

It's funny how time helps us to sort out things and help them make sense. That is exactly what Jett had been. He was a conquest and nothing more. She wanted to prove she could have him.

"Well, don't worry if she's there, Cassandra and I will handle her," Olivia said with a gleam in her eye.

I told her, "Liv. I'm not interested in getting even. It's haunted me long enough. I moved on and I'm happy. I'm the one that won!"

Olivia smiled and said, "I still don't like her and if I see her I will give her a piece of my mind." Her red head temper was flaring again. "You don't treat your friends like that and get away with it!" she said and pounded her fists on the kitchen table for emphasis.

"That's why I have you guys. And we are going to have a ball in Dallas. I can't wait to have tea at The Adolphus Hotel!" I shrieked.

"I'm looking forward to that Amelia, but not as much as I am to going to Ft. Worth!" Olivia said and jumped up to do a short jig.

"Speaking of Dallas and Ft. Worth, I better grab Emma and head home to pack. Thanks for the lemonade iced tea," I said and turned. "Can we keep the whole Katherine, Jett incident between you and me?" I requested.

"You can count on me, Amelia. I can't promise I won't let her have it though if I see her," she said and laughed.

"Shane doesn't think she will come, so maybe getting worked up is just a waste of time," I said, rather hopefully.

Olivia and I hugged and headed outside. She had barn chores to finish and I had some major packing to do. I needed to make sure I looked my best at the reunion.

Emma had just finished her lesson, and we drove home for a simple salmon dinner with fresh asparagus and for dessert, a strawberry rhubarb pie I had baked the day before. It would be the last rhubarb of the season.

Emma and Charlie had homework, and Shane helped me get the suitcases out of the attic. I started laying out my wardrobe for the trip.

"Do you think this dress will be appropriate for the cocktail reception?" I asked holding up a slender black sheath dress.

"I thought I would wear my large pearl earrings and sling back pumps," I continued, looking at Shane for confirmation of my wardrobe pick.

"I think you are going to look sensational!" he reassured me. "You aren't trying to dress to impress Jett are you?" he teased.

"I don't even know if he is going, and, quite frankly, this isn't about him. I want to make sure I keep up with Cassandra," I smiled.

"You always look good to me, sweetie!" he said as he nuzzled the nape of my neck. "Just don't forget who's waiting at home for you."

"How could I ever?" I gently reminded him.

"When is Aunt Alice getting here?" I asked and started my mental check off list.

"Tomorrow morning around nine o'clock in the morning, so you will have time to go over everything at the tea room with her before you fly out. Don't worry! She's an old pro at this!" Shane told me.

And she was. Thank goodness for Shane's Aunt Alice. I could count on her to fill in whenever I had an illness or needed a few days off. She simply followed my carefully detailed recipes and kept the kitchen running in tip top shape.

I had also kept reservations to a minimum so she wouldn't be too overwhelmed. She had restaurant experience and had run a large commercial kitchen for years. She thought the tea room was "small and cute."

"You make sure Aunt Alice has my cell phone number so she can call me if she gets overwhelmed with too many guests. I will call and check in several times a day with her to make sure everything goes smoothly," I told him.

"Amelia, this trip is to get your mind off the tea room and to enjoy your friends," he reminded me. "I think Aunt Alice will be just fine. And remember, she can call me and I will be there in five minutes flat. We've got it covered!" he reassured me.

I hoped so, I thought, and continued to pack.

Chapter Five

"Mrs. Reynolds's, we'll be landing at Love Field Airport in approximately seven minutes," our pilot said from the cockpit of the private jet.

"Thank you, Albert!" Cassandra said. She was smartly dressed in an aubergine Christian Dior pant suit. It was something she had picked up in Paris on her last shopping trip. A three stranded black pearl choker with matching earrings completed the package. She looked like she had stepped off the pages of *Vogue*.

"What a wonderful trip already and we haven't even landed in Dallas," Sarah sighed. Traveling in the corporate jet had been a thrill for Sarah. She smiled with contentment as she ran her hands along the buttery soft leather of her seat.

"How much does a jet like this set you back, Cassandra?" always practical Olivia asked.

"This is supposed to be a pleasure trip, Liv," Cassandra reminded her. "We are not talking about business this weekend."

"I get it. Probably three Riverbend Farms put together," Olivia continued. She had dressed for Dallas in her black and white snake skin boots, her dress Wrangler jeans and a bright yellow Mexican inspired embroidered top. She wore her red hair down and naturally curly today. A touch of clear lip gloss and mascara set off her tanned face.

"We have a car meeting us at the airport and I thought after we checked into the hotel, you could give us a tour of Dallas, Amelia," Cassandra suggested.

"I'm starving!" Olivia said as she helped herself to another stuffed mushroom cap. "Can we go somewhere for some Tex Mex?" she asked hopefully.

"Of course, but I was thinking of an old hang out near campus called "Snuffer's," I told them. "They have THE BEST cheese fries and burgers anywhere. It's where most of the freshmen gained the infamous freshmen fifteen!"

"Oh, the dreaded fifteen pound weight gain," Sarah said. "I always worried about that when I was at UT." Sarah smoothed her prairie skirt with ruffled petticoat peeking from underneath. Her short sleeved scalloped blouse was the perfect accompaniment to her look inspired by *Little House on the Prairie* meets *Hee Haw*. She still managed to pull it off and look totally adorable.

"Well, it doesn't look like you've ever had to worry about your weight, Sarah!" I said. "And remember if you tell anyone here that you graduated from UT, they will think you mean University of Texas, not Tennessee," I said.

"Aren't there school colors orange and white also?" Olivia asked, and popped another stuffed mushroom in her mouth.

"Different shade of orange. Texas is more of a burnt orange," I said.

"I still can't believe you left home and went so far away to college. I don't think I could have done that," Sarah admitted as she looked out the window at Dallas laid out below us like a patchwork quilt.

"My parents pretty much left it up to me where I attended college. I had a lot of friends at Camp Nakanawa for Girls in Crossville, Tennessee who were from Texas and I had visited them over the years. I have always liked Texas," I told them.

"Yeah, but it's so flat!" Olivia exclaimed. "No views of the mountains and very few trees. It has lots of flat land perfect for cattle farming, though," she added.

"Perfect for cowboys, is what you mean, Liv!" Cassandra teased her. "Where there are cattle, there's bound to be a cowboy!"

Albert put the jet down smoothly, and within minutes, he had taxied to a stop. The flight crew helped us down the ladder to the waiting town car limo. Just as soon as our luggage was stowed away, we were headed downtown to the Adolphus Hotel. We pulled up to the Baroque beauty, built in 1912, which was remarked as being "the most beautiful building west of Venice."

"Oh, Cassandra!" I gasped. "I had no idea when you said we would be staying at a friend's hotel, that it would be so grand." And it was from the twenty one soaring stories, to the gorgeous burled wood paneling throughout the hotel. I suddenly felt underdressed! I had worn a simple black turtleneck cashmere sweater with charcoal grey dress slacks and black pumps. I felt as though a tiara and ball gown would have been far more appropriate.

We checked in and were taken up to our luxury suite for the weekend.

"Oh, my goodness!" Sarah squealed as we walked through the handsomely appointed living room. "There's a garden terrace and look at the view of down town!"

"That's Reunion Arena over there," I said and pointed to the large orb in the skyline. That's where they have ice hockey games and some of biggest concerts in the area have been held there. I saw Aerosmith and Michael Jackson perform there when I was a student. I love to see it at night when the arena is lit up. It's quite spectacular."

"Have you ever been to the top floor?" Sarah asked, her huge brown eyes taking in the Dallas skyline.

"Yes. I celebrated my birthday at the restaurant on the top floor. It rotates, so the view is constantly changing. It was really a neat experience," I told her, suddenly feeling wistful.

"Sounds romantic, Amelia. What was his name?" Cassandra quizzed me.

I quickly looked over at Olivia to see if she had let the cat out of the bag about Jett. She raised her eyebrows and shrugged her shoulders indicating she had not said a word.

"No one special," I quickly covered. "It was my twenty-first birthday and a great memory," I quickly changed the subject. "So who feels like Snuffer's, and their world famous cheese fries?"

"Count me in, Amelia!" Olivia raised her hand.

"Sounds great!" Cassandra agreed.

"Me too!" Sarah chimed in.

Snuffer's was an established Dallas landmark that opened in 1978 on Greenville Avenue close to the SMU campus. The cheddar cheese fries have been called "A rite of passage" by *The Dallas Morning News*. The gigantic hamburgers are legendary. The lunch crowd is a mixture of college students and Dallas area business people. There's nothing quite as exquisite as a hot basket of Snuffers cheddar cheese fries.

"Good call, Amelia!" Olivia smiled and licked her fingers. "This is my kind of place!" And it was. The laid back atmosphere was a good fit for Olivia's down-to-earth personality. "I haven't seen any cowboys yet," she said looking rather disappointed.

"We will have to go to Ft. Worth for real cowboys," I laughed and told her.

"But when I watched the television show, *Dallas*," Sarah said, "everyone walked around wearing cowboy hats and boots."

"Honey, that's just TV!" Cassandra laughed and elbowed Sarah playfully.

"I never saw any cowboys in Dallas," I explained to Sarah. "I saw lots of boots, though."

"It's sort of like what most people think about Tennessee," Cassandra said. "They think we don't wear shoes and that we are all related to Dolly Parton."

"I can't eat another bite!" I groaned. "How 'bout we walk off our lunch by doing a little shopping at North Park Mall?"

"Is it nicer than the mall in Dogwood Cove?" Sarah asked, wiping mustard from the corner of her mouth.

"Oh, honey is it ever!" Cassandra cooed. "They have the very best stores like Giorgio Armani, Versace and Kate Spade."

"Fine with me as long as you don't try to take me for another make over," Olivia said and shot a dirty look at Cassandra.

"Look, I was trying to help a friend in need," Cassandra protested. "Your eyebrows were desperate for some shaping."

"I thought you looked really pretty after your makeover, Liv!" I enthusiastically said.

"Well," she paused, "I have been keeping up with the eyebrow waxing after since then, if you haven't noticed."

We sat stunned at her admission. Olivia really did care more about her appearance than her hard exterior let on. She just didn't let too many people in on the fact that she had a girly side.

"Oh, Liv!" Cassandra threw her arms around her and hugged her hard. "I am so proud of you!" she said and praised her.

"Don't get carried away!" Olivia pushed her back. "You're not going to put me in pink and start dressing me like a Mary Kay sales rep."

"Well, we could pick out a few new outfits for you while we are shopping," Cassandra said hopefully. She never gave up trying to help Olivia reach her true fashion potential. Olivia, on the other hand was more like her stubborn mares who just dug in their heels and wouldn't move. And her fashion sense worked for her. She had such a natural beauty about her that didn't really need much embellishing.

"If I give in to that, you'll be trying to drag me to Fashion Week with you," Olivia snipped as she rolled her eyes.

"Okay, let's get going before this turns into a bad version of *The Devil Wears Prada*." I paid the bill. We then drove the short trip to North Park Mall.

Chapter Six

Several shopping bags and four hours later, we returned to the Adolphus Hotel exhausted from our extended shopping excursion.

"If we walked in one more store, I think my feet would have fallen off," Olivia complained as she took off her boots and rubbing her feet.

"Well, you were the one so interested in buying a new dress for the cocktail party tomorrow night. How many stores did we go to until we found the perfect one?" Cassandra turned and asked us.

"I think six," Sarah guessed. "But we all found some great things in the process. I love this hand beaded jewelry. It will go with so many of my outfits. I love it!"

Sarah had definitely made a good choice. She was quite pleased with her selections, and they suited her carefree spirit. She seemed to be much more like her old self.

"I'm going to hang up my new dress for tomorrow night," Olivia said as she smiled and took her new purchases out of her shopping bags. She seemed quite proud of herself.

"Hey, before you get started with a fashion show, I have a surprise for all of you!" Cassandra said enthusiastically.

"I hope it doesn't involve walking or I am going to have blisters for sure," Olivia warned and continued hanging up her new cocktail dress.

"You won't even have to wear shoes or clothes for that matter," Cassandra said and rubbed her hands together laughing. She was enjoying the suspense.

"Okay, I give up," I told Cassandra and plopped down on the sofa. "I don't care where we go as long as we don't have to move!" Every muscle in my foot was sore and throbbing.

"Just slip into something comfortable and be ready to go in twenty minutes," she directed us.

Though we could have all taken a short nap, we were excited about this mysterious surprise. After freshening up a bit and changing into more comfortable clothes, we all were ready to go.

"It's just a short drive from here," Cassandra informed us.

We were surprised when we drove to McKinney Avenue in Uptown Dallas not too far from Snuffer's on Greenville Avenue. The West Village area is an eclectic mix of dining and shops including The Hard Rock Café and Dallas Museum of Art.

"Carl, we'll stop here," Cassandra said to our limo driver. She turned and told us that we would be riding the McKinney Avenue Trolley to our destination.

"Oh, how fun! An authentic trolley car!" Sarah exclaimed. "I've always wanted to ride one of these."

It was a great way to see the sights on McKinney. Between the restaurants, boutique shops and art galleries, it really was a worthwhile area to visit. It had a certain urban vibe to it.

"Where are we going?" I leaned over and whispered to Cassandra.

She replied, "You'll see. Shane and I cooked this little surprise up, especially for you."

We soon exited at the next trolley stop and found ourselves standing outside of Spa Habitat, voted Dallas' best spa several years in a row. I was speechless. How perfect. A spa evening!

I hugged Cassandra around the neck and blurted, "Oh, you two thought of everything!" We were soon ushered into a dressing area to change into our robes.

Our spa hostess, Linda, told us that we would be experiencing the "Green Freak" spa package. It would include an organic massage, organic foot ritual, organic facial, eco buff and spa dinner. We would also be keeping our robes.

"I can't believe you and Shane planned this," I said amazed. No wonder Shane had been so secretive before I left. I could just picture him researching all the spas in Dallas and selecting this one for its environmentally friendly products — something we support in our business as well. More and more people were becoming interested in organics and the supporting environmentally friendly causes.

"Shane is the one who heard about this place," Cassandra shared with us. "They were recently voted 'Best Spa Package' by *Day Spa Magazine*. Plus, Shane loved the fact that everything here is organic since you also have a green business as well," she said.

"These robes are so comfy and made from organically grown cotton!" Sarah cooed. "I love it!"

"Shane is a keeper, Amelia," Olivia said and smiled. I knew that she was looking for someone special too. And she would find him. It would be hard for someone to measure up to her high standards and hard work ethic. But we all knew, when Olivia did fall, she would fall hard.

"Ladies, would you like to begin your organic body massages now?" Linda asked as she led us down the hall way to the Asian inspired spa treatment room. "I can take two of you at a time for the massage and two at a time for the organic foot ritual."

Between the foot reflexology, the three stage body buffing with grapefruit mint or vanilla honey exfoliating scrub and the hydrating foot and hand treatment, we were all like limp noodles when we were finished a few hours later.

Olivia really was impressed. "You have no idea how good that feels to someone who does farm chores day in and day out!" she said. "I needed that so much. Why can't we have a spa like this in Dogwood Cove?" she groaned.

"Not a bad idea, Liv. I would certainly go often!" I added. In fact Shane and I had been working together with an aromatherapy specialist to develop a new spa product line infused with tea, of course! This would go over well in Dogwood Cove.

"I think I am going to have sweet dreams tonight," Sarah yawned and closed her eyes. "I am in a zone of total bliss."

"Me too," Cassandra added. "This has been amazing."

"Thank you Linda!" We all said and hugged our spa professionals and thanked them profusely along with leaving generous gratuities. It had been worth every penny to feel this recharged.

The town car was waiting out front and we all were quiet as we drove back to the hotel. I was especially reflective tonight, wondering what lay in store at tomorrow's cocktail party and who might be attending. Little did I know that tonight's serene atmosphere would be the last bit of peace I would experience for quite some time.

Chapter Seven

"I think I will try a pot of your jasmine pearls," Olivia told the waiter in the grandly appointed French tea salon of the Adolphus Hotel. She looked smart today in one of her new outfits Cassandra had helped her select. The pumpkin colored suede skirt and matching jacket brought out the copper highlights in her hair. She was enjoying herself and the attention she was receiving from the male wait staff.

"Olivia, I am so proud of you!" Cassandra boasted and patted her hand. "No one at home would recognize you out of your Wranglers."

"Let's not get too carried away, Cassandra," Olivia reminded her. "I do know how to dress up and every now and again. It's just not all that practical for me to dress up and work on the farm."

Olivia was right about that. I couldn't see her driving her bright green John Deere tractor in these high heeled chocolate brown boots. She did look like a million dollars. I was glad she had given in to Cassandra's urging to play dress up while we were shopping at North Park Mall.

"Ohh," I exclaimed as the waiter poured my tea selection, a black Assam tea with malty undertones. I inhaled its heavenly aroma. I was going to savor every sip of this.

Sarah had ordered a pot of spicy Marsala Chai. Cassandra was indulging in a Ceylon tea from Sri Lanka flavored with raspberry. Both seemed happy with their choices.

"What a great idea to come here for afternoon tea," Sarah commented as she picked up her pitcher of milk and added a splash to her tea. "I just love chai. The combination of cloves, cardamom, cinnamon, and peppercorns remind me of autumn. Mmm!"

"My raspberry tea reminds me of one of our raspberry filled candies." Cassandra laughed. "This would make a great truffle."

I agreed and commented, "I think that would be an excellent idea!" Tea infused truffles were quite a trend in both the chocolate and tea world. In fact, tea infused foods were served in some of the most trendy restaurants in Hollywood, Boston, New York and D.C. We had learned a lot about tea infused foods on our "Tea Cruise" and I had also studied recipes from Master Tea Blender, John Harney of Harney and Sons Tea Company. His latest book featured recipes using tea in marinades, sauces, desserts, and entrees.

"Amelia, between your knowledge of tea and my knowledge of chocolate, it would seem we should be able to collaborate on a tea and chocolate line of candies," Cassandra suggested.

"I would be the first in line to try it," Sarah said delighted at the idea. She looked quite chic today in a red suit with faux fur collar and cuffs, which was a tribute to "Jackie O." She complemented the outfit with a jet bead broach, black gloves and vintage black patent leather handbag. She was a throwback to the 1960s and wore it well. All she was needed was a pillbox hat.

"Shane and I have been looking into developing other products featuring our tea," I told them. "I think adding tea infused chocolates would also do well. In fact, I have tried several truffle recipes on our tea trays and they have been overwhelming popular with our guests," I informed them.

"Are you talking about those chocolates you gave me for my birthday last year?" Olivia asked me. Her eyes lit up!

"Yes. Those were the orange blossom oolong truffles," I told her. I loved the way the tea was infused with orange blossoms, not only scenting the tea, but giving it an exotic flavor as well. It paired well with chocolate and made a distinct flavor combination.

"Those were so wonderful that I didn't even share them," she joked and looked around the table sheepishly. Olivia had gobbled up the entire box in a matter of an hour.

"We noticed, Liv!" Cassandra jested with her. "We were all hoping to have one, but I guess we will have to wait until our birthdays!"

I loved the way this tight knit group could banter back and forth, but still have so much love between the four of us.

"To 'The Traveling Tea Ladies!'" I toasted and we each raised our tea cups and gently clinked them together.

Just then our server presented our table with a gorgeous three-tiered tea tray. There were currant scones with Devonshire cream and lemon curd, thinly sliced cucumber tea sandwiches, smoked salmon with capers and a lovely selection of pastries and tarts. The blueberry sour cream tart was by far my favorite.

"Oh, my stars!" Cassandra exclaimed. "This has been so wonderful, and I just love the ambiance of this dining room. I wish I could hire their decorator."

"Your house looks like a miniature version of Versailles as it is, Cassandra," I told her. "You don't need any help decorating or redecorating."

We all shook our heads in agreement. Cassandra had an eye for color, furniture placement and entertaining. Many Reynolds's Candies contract negotiations had been held in the living room of her Dogwood Cove home. It wasn't unusual to find Cassandra and Doug entertaining one of their celebrity friends on the weekends in their majestic lakefront mansion.

"Speaking of Versailles, I am planning a trip in the spring to Paris to develop some new chocolate recipes for Reynolds's," she informed us.

"Ooh la, la and kiss my grits," Olivia teased.

"How wonderful, Cassandra," I said.

"Maybe you should think about coming with me and developing your tea truffles with our head chef," she suggested. It was obvious she was serious about the offer.

"Do you mean it?" I asked her. I couldn't believe the opportunity she was extending. I didn't quite know what to think.

"Of course I mean it. This isn't the first time I've thought about it and with your tea education and culinary experience, this would be a sure fire thing," Cassandra predicted.

For the first time in the last few weeks, I felt excited! I had been focusing so much on what I was saying goodbye to that I had not begun to realize how much I had to look forward to.

"This calls for some champagne, girls," Olivia declared. "We have a lot to toast."

"I'll say," Sarah agreed. "How exciting, Amelia! If you hadn't decided to sell The Pink Dogwood, this may not have ever happened."

Sarah was right. I was beginning to see a bright future, a future in which I would be working with Shane on a daily basis and really stretching my creativity. And if a perk was working surrounded by the delightful aroma of tea and now chocolate, I could live with that!

I felt a lift in my step as we returned to our suite to get ready for the cocktail party to be held at the Meadows Museum on the SMU campus. The museum held a special place in my heart since I was a marketing intern for the Meadows Museum when I was a student. I fell in love with the Spanish Golden Age collection that included works by Goya, Murillo and Picasso. My job had been to write press releases for upcoming art shows and to help create a catalogue for the museum. There were sculptures by Rodin and a beautiful sculpture garden in the plaza. It was the perfect back drop for a cocktail party.

Our hotel suite was large enough to accommodate the primping needs of four ladies. We all took turns zipping dresses, fastening necklaces and assisting each other with makeup. Olivia even consented to eye liner tonight.

I was especially nervous, not quite sure who would be there, but confident that with my good friends by my side, the evening would be fine, or at least I hoped it would be.

My simple sleeveless black sheath dress was elegantly understated. I wore my hair in an upsweep reminiscent of Grace Kelly and decided to wear my pearl and diamond earrings. Because October evenings can become chilly, I decided to take a matching black wrap.

"Are we ready, ladies?" Cassandra asked the group. She looked stunning in a champagne colored pant suit with a textured tapestry jacket, silk top and matching lounge pants. The honey highlights in her hair stood out even more than usual. She wore an antique pearl broach and strands of pearls and Swarovski crystals in cascading lengths. She oozed class!

"I'm ready," Olivia announced. She was wearing an emerald green velvet cocktail dress with her hair in loose spiral curls. She reminded me of a petite Nicole Kidman tonight. She had that clear complexion, red hair and tiny frame for which women might kill!

Sarah came out of the bedroom wearing a highly embellished Indian sari in variations of gold and burgundy. Her black silk pants and gold gladiator sandals kept the look updated and dressy for tonight's affair.

"Sarah, I never would have thought of wearing that. You look fantastic!" I blurted.

"It's comfortable and yet exotic at the same time," she confessed smiling at me.

"You're not going to do the dance of the seven veils, are you?" Olivia joked and began spinning around the room holding a hotel hand towel like a veil in front of her face.

"I have been taking belly dancing classes on Tuesday nights and I've become quite good," she boasted as she swung her hips from side to side.

"Sarah!" I cried! "I've never seen this side of you!" We all started dancing around the living room of our suite.

"Okay, ladies," Cassandra cautioned, slightly out of breath from our dancing. "We better high tail it before our coach turns into a pumpkin."

The drive from down town to the SMU campus was a relatively short one. As dusk was approaching, the entrance at Mockingbird Lane and Bishop Boulevard was lit as if a Hollywood director had waited for just the right lighting to create the perfect shot. It was a breath taking glimpse down the lane of ancient Oak trees lining the row of buildings leading your eye to the focal center piece, Dallas Hall. Built in 1911 and fashioned after Thomas Jefferson's Rotunda on the University of Virginia campus, it was a spectacular sight to behold. Its rounded copper roof had aged to a patina. This building was the first built on this campus and was listed with the National Historic Register.

"How beautiful!" Sarah spoke softly. "I can't believe you went to school here!"

Carl drove the complete horseshoe of Bishop's Boulevard to let us take in the beauty of this campus. He stopped in front of Dallas Hall, majestically lit with up lights. Its massive fountain bubbled at the center of the expansive lawn.

I felt a lump in my throat as I thought back to all the classes I had taken in those hallowed halls and how I had enjoyed feeling as though I was walking in the footsteps of history.

"Is this where you took most of your classes, Amelia?" Sarah asked.

"No, most of mine were in the Owens Art Center," I said and remembered walking past the bronze sculpture of the three nymphs every day on my way to class. It only seemed fitting that the Meadows School of the Arts graduation ceremony was held in the sculpture garden surrounded by the bronze creations that had become a part of our daily routine.

We slowly drove past Perkins chapel where so many weddings were held for couples who had met as undergraduates at SMU. There were many Saturday afternoons when I had witnessed happy wedding parties exiting the chapel in a hail of rice. It was where Jett and I had planned on having our wedding ceremony. We also passed Smith Hall which had been my home my sophomore year adjacent to the Perkins School of Theology. This is where Katherine and I had roomed together.

Carl completed the horseshoe and headed back to Meadows Museum, just past the campus entrance on the right. Valet attendants were waiting to open our door and usher us up the stairs to the cocktail party already in progress.

Olivia gently took my elbow and whispered in my ear, "Remember, Amelia, I've got your back," she winked as a sign of her support.

"Thank you, Liv," and I truly meant it. My stomach was doing flip flops at this point. I concentrated on making it up the steps without too many bumbles.

"Ladies, may I take a picture for the alumni committee?" A young man with a camera and tripod asked as we entered the museum.

We stood together, with our arms around each other. "Remember girls, it's one, two, three, TEA!" I teased them. We did that for all our pictures.

"TEA!" We called out in chorus.

As we stepped inside the museum, we were greeted by a registration table for name tags.

"Welcome, class of 1990!" a platinum blonde Miss Texas look-a-like enthusiastically greeted us. "If y'all will tell me your names, I'll get your name badges."

"I hate these things," Olivia complained as she pinned on her name badge. "Maybe I don't want just anyone knowing my name. You just can't be too careful these days." She was still frowning as she smoothed her dress.

"Liv, I don't think anyone is going to bother you at such a nice function," Cassandra chided her. "This isn't a honky-tonk bar, you know. The men here might be a tad more respectable."

"I'm not so sure about that," Liv mumbled and shot me a conspirator's glance.

"This is just so beautiful!" Sarah said with an awed expression. "I can just imagine you here during your coed days cataloging all these beautiful works of art."

"Back then, this museum had not been built. Everything was housed in the Owens Art Center. This museum has been a wonderful addition to the school," I told them.

I brought Shane here during my last campus visit. We both had enjoyed perusing the different galleries show casing the largest collection of Spanish Art outside of Spain from the 1550s to Picasso. Right now I wished he were by my side. I missed him and Emma and Charlie so much. I was having a wonderful time, but it would have been even more perfect with all of them there.

Our foursome walked into the main foyer area of the Meadows Museum. They had several bar areas set up including one area dedicated exclusively to tequila tasting. Apparently tequila tasting is similar to a wine tasting with the subtle variations depending on the maker, the maker's process and the Blue Agave's growing environment. Tonight they were serving eight featured tequilas in a tulip shaped wine glass with plenty of tortillas and water for cleansing the palate between sampling.

"No, thank you!" Olivia politely told the server who offered her a glass of Pepe Lopez. "The last time I had tequila I rode the mechanical bull at The Lazy Spur and nearly broke my back." She scared all of us that night and after what turned out to be a mild case of whiplash, she was back in the saddle again. Yeah, maybe tequila was wise to avoid this evening!

As we strolled along the gallery, there were a maze of different rooms, featuring different artists and their collections. In the center of each room were tables draped in black linens with a tempting array of hors d'oeuvres. I helped myself to a wonderful blue cheese and apricot spread on rye cocktail triangles and began walking around the gallery.

"Amelia, you need to try the stuffed figs. They are scrumptious!" Sarah said enthusiastically. She really did look stunning tonight in her sari. That's what I loved so much about her. She had a willingness to take risks in her wardrobe and she had a natural enthusiasm for life. There was nothing phony about Sarah. She had an almost child-like innocence about her. Sarah was really enjoying our trip and I was glad. She seemed to be in much better spirits. Maybe she had figured out what to do about her job at the library.

"Is this a Picasso?" Sarah exclaimed, her eyes widening in total disbelief. "I have never seen one in person!"

We were both admiring the abstract, when I sensed someone behind us. I assumed it was Cassandra and Olivia. I turned quickly, smiling to include them.

"Amelia, I thought that was you. You look beautiful." Standing before me was Jett Rollins, all six foot three inches of him. I momentarily stood there with a look of shock on my face. I guess I had been hoping he wouldn't come. I had not prepared myself to see him again. He looked good. He was a little gray around the temples of his dark brown hair and not quite as thin, but he looked like he had kept up his workout routine from years of running track. He was wearing a dark black suit with a lavender dress shirt that brought out his blue eyes.

"Hi, I'm Sarah!" Sarah said, quickly extending her hand and giving Jett a warm smile. "I am Amelia's friend from Dogwood Cove." Thank goodness for Sarah's quick intervention! By now, I had recovered and shook the cobwebs from my brain.

"Well, Jett. Nice to see you," I told him, controlling my voice and body language, trying not to convey much emotion. "Where is Laura tonight?"

"She's at home with the new twins," he said and began taking out his cell phone. "Look, I've got pictures."

He proudly showed us pictures of his stunning wife Laura, a former Miss Kentucky, holding two babies in her lap, one swaddled in pink and one in blue. They really were adorable. I was happy for him.

"How sweet! What are their names?" Sarah asked, genuinely interested.

"Jacob and Bonnie," he said with softness in his voice. "We weren't really sure we would ever have children. They are our little miracles." I had never seen Jett so emotional before. This was a different side of him. But, babies will do that. They pull at one's heart strings.

"Congratulations, Jett. It looks like you have a beautiful family," I told him.

"Speaking of family, how is yours?" he asked. "I read in the alumni news about your wedding and the birth of your children."

"They are wonderful. Shane is handling some business deals while I am here with my good friends. Emma is fourteen, Charlie is twelve. They are home with Shane and Aunt Alice for the weekend," I told him, as I missed Shane and the kids even more.

Just then Cassandra and Olivia joined our little circle. Olivia quickly read Jett's name badge and recognition set in. She raised her eyebrows in a show of support.

"Jett Rollins, these are my very good friends, Olivia Rivers and Cassandra Reynolds from Dogwood Cove," I said and introduced them.

"Hello, Jett," Cassandra said extending her hand in a nonchalant manner. "So very pleased to meet you." Cassandra had no idea of the history between us. She had heard Shane mention a "Jett" in the kitchen and the reference as "an old boyfriend," but nothing more than that.

"Jett," Olivia said in a business-like manner. She nodded curtly at him and turned away as if interested in the painting over her shoulder. That was Olivia. She just couldn't pretend to like someone she didn't.

"Amelia and I were just catching up on our families," Jett told them.

"Oh, yes!" Olivia piped up. "Amelia has a WONDERFUL husband who adores her and two precious children. She is so LUCKY and HAPPY!" she said emphasizing the "L" and the "H." It was obvious to Jett that Olivia was being protective.

"That's all I ever wanted for her," he admitted to the group but looked me straight in the eyes. I knew he was feeling bad for the way things had ended.

"Jett has new twins with his beautiful wife, Laura," I informed them and shot Olivia a look that screamed, "Back Down Now!" I doubted she would, though.

"How wonderful," Cassandra added. "Is Laura here with you?" She looked around expecting to meet his wife.

"No, she's at home with the babies," Jett answered her. "She insisted I come." He turned his attention back to me.

"Yoo Hoo, Amelia!" I heard from across the gallery. "I heard you would be here."

"Leslie Lane!" I squealed and gave her a huge bear hug.

Leslie had majored in theater at SMU. She and Katherine had always competed for the lead in the department's productions. Leslie and I had been close friends and the three of us had rented a house our junior and senior years. She was aware of what had happened with Jett and Katherine. In fact, Leslie had been my maid of honor at my wedding.

"Jett Rollins . . . well, well, well," Leslie said, her voice dripping with sarcasm. "Long time no see. I guess the last time I saw you was . . . wait, let me think about this." This little exchange was becoming very uncomfortable for all of us.

"Leslie, I see you haven't changed a bit," Jett fired at her. "Ladies, if you'll excuse me. Amelia, I hope we have the chance to catch up later." He turned and walked out of the gallery.

"Leslie, I can't believe you are here! You look beautiful!" I exclaimed. Her smoldering cat-like green eyes and black hair had made her the envy of many coeds at SMU. The years had done little to change that. Tonight she was wearing a black strapless dress, her ample bosom barely contained. She wore a gold asp arm bracelet, its green emerald eyes mirroring her own.

I often wondered why she had not "made it" yet in the acting world. Oh, she had talent. She was a gifted singer, dancer and actress, but other than a few supporting roles on Broadway, she had not had her big break yet. Shane and I recently had seen her in a production of *Wicked* on Broadway. She was wonderful.

"I flew in from New York this afternoon. I couldn't miss the opportunity to see everyone again," she said and squeezed my hands. Leslie had been a loyal friend to me. When I left for London in 1990, she was the one who packed all my belongings and put them in storage so I wouldn't have to come back to the house and deal with Katherine.

"Leslie, you remember Olivia, Sarah and Cassandra?" I said and turned to take in the entire group.

"Yes! Of course," she said as hugs were exchanged all around.

"Cassandra and I recently saw each other at the Tony awards," Leslie reminded us.

"Wasn't that fun?" Cassandra squealed. "I think Hugh Jackman did a wonderful job hosting it this year."

"Oh, I forgot you two travel in the same circles," Olivia said and rolled her eyes. "Hugh Jackman, George Clooney, Angelina Jolie . . . "

"Katherine Gold," Leslie interrupted as the paparazzi cameras began flashing, snapping pictures of Katherine's entrance into the museum.

Katherine had a white fur stole draped around her shoulders. Her body hugging gold Versace gown was cut dangerously low in the back and high at the thigh. She had obviously had a lot of double sided tape carefully placed in strategic areas. She looked smoking hot tonight and acted like she knew it.

"Katherine, over here!" The paparazzi called to her. "Miss Gold, Could you show us your dress. Who are you wearing tonight?"

"She's wearing Versace," a stern woman in a navy pen striped business suit addressed the Dallas television crews. Her three inch navy pumps and bobbed hair cut were a sharp contrast to Katherine's six inch gold stilettos and long platinum mane. "If you'll hurry and take a few more shots and allow Miss Gold to enjoy her reunion," the woman ordered.

Katherine was eating up the attention with a spoon! She posed with her back towards the cameras and looked vampy over one shoulder. She turned to face the cameras, her head thrown back and to the side, blowing kisses at the reporters.

"Thank you, thank you. If you'll let Miss Gold through, please," the very efficient woman shouted.

"Is that her?" Olivia asked and looked at me. "I really think she looks desperate wearing that dress. If she doesn't watch it, she may have a 'wardrobe malfunction.'" Olivia was referring to the infamous Janet Jackson Super Bowl snafu a few years ago.

"I concur one hundred percent, Olivia!" Leslie said snidely. "Just look at her. She was always so needy for attention."

Leslie had a point. After living with Katherine a few years, I really got to know her quite intimately. Anytime we had company over, male or female, Katherine insisted on being the center of attention—especially if it was male attention. There had been more than one of Leslie's dates who had fallen victim to her wily ways. Over the years, she had learned not to bring her dates home or to arrange to have them over when Katherine was gone for the weekend.

"She's like a praying mantis," Leslie continued. "She devours every male in her path."

"Well, enough about her," I said, my stomach tied up in knots. "I think I will go try that tequila bar." I headed in the opposite direction of the throng of Katherine Gold fan club members who were following her around like a litter of puppies after their mother.

"Wait up! I'm coming too, Amelia," Liv cried after me. I was glad she was there for the support. Sarah and Cassandra continued their conversation with Leslie and waved goodbye at us from across the gallery.

"Two Pepe Lopez's, please," I requested from the bartender.

"I like Leslie," Olivia stated. "She's a straight shooter."

"Much like you," I agreed as we clinked glasses. "Boy would I like to disappear about now," I admitted.

"Don't be ridiculous!" Olivia chastised me. "If anyone should be embarrassed to be at this reunion it should be Katherine. You didn't get caught with your roommate's fiancée. You didn't plunge a dagger into YOUR friend's back. You didn't break up an engagement. She should be ashamed to show her face here after what she did!" Olivia ranted. Her fiery temper was stoked. Tequila may not have been a good idea.

"Thank you, sweetie," I hugged her and gave her a quick kiss on the cheek. "You've always known the right thing to say."

"Look, its obvious Jett feels bad. I don't excuse his behavior, you know how I feel about cheating, but from what they print in the tabloids, no man can say no to Katherine Gold," Olivia fumed. "She's been linked to everyone from Tom Cruise to Brad Pitt. She's a home wrecker." Olivia had finished her tequila and was steering us towards the shrimp wrapped bacon appetizers. She popped one in her mouth and put three more on a small white plate.

"Have you ever thought that Jett has a lot of regrets?" she suggested as she looked at me, her eyes softening.

"Yeah, I think he regrets he got caught!" I often wondered if he would have told me if I had not walked in on them. "And quite frankly, it doesn't matter to me. My life worked out the way it was supposed to. I don't regret what happened. It was a blessing. Shane and the kids are my whole life," I admitted.

"You were lucky, Amelia," Olivia reassured me. "You ended up with happily-ever-after. I'm not so sure Katherine has found hers yet," she said with authority in her voice. "That young Hollywood 'boy toy' she's dating is just using her to further his career. You can bet on that," Olivia pointed out.

"When did you become an authority on celebrity gossip?" I asked her, teasingly.

"I read *People* and *US Weekly*," she admitted sheepishly. "Just don't let Cassandra know. She'd never let me live it down since I give her such a hard time about her 'Hollyweird' friends." She chuckled and popped another shrimp in her mouth. "I'm starving. Don't they have a side of beef or something substantial here?" she whined.

"Oh, Olivia, you and your hearty appetite!" Cassandra said siding up to us. She fluffed Olivia's spiral curls and continued. "Sarah and I were just having a very nice chat with Leslie. She's going to be auditioning for a movie next week," Cassandra stated.

"Really! How great!" I said and meant it. Leslie was due for her big break. "She didn't mention a word of it to me."

"Well, I think she is very nervous about this one. Ron Howard is directing it," Cassandra said.

"Wow, Ron Howard! I would be nervous too," I agreed.

"I am hoping to get Leslie to visit Dogwood Cove and do an evening with our symphony. It would be a sold-out show for sure," Cassandra predicted.

"That's a great idea. I would love for her to come to Dogwood Cove again. It's been a few years. I think an invitation from Cassandra Reynolds would have some clout," I giggled.

"I'll keep working on her," Cassandra said. "Amelia, are you okay?" she turned facing me and looked into my eyes. "Leslie filled me in on Jett and Katherine. It sounds like that was a horrible time for you." Cassandra was truly concerned. "Why didn't you tell me when I was out at your place the other night? I could just shoot myself for going on and on about you and Katherine being roommates," she lamented.

"Cassandra, all that is ancient history. I don't want you to feel bad about bringing up Katherine. It's just not a topic I enjoy, that's all. That mess was twenty years ago. Shane and I are such a perfect fit, that I just feel it all happened for a reason," I reassured her.

"She's a better woman than I," Olivia interrupted. "I personally would have tossed Katherine Gold out by her 'goldilocks!'" Olivia threatened loudly. The attendant at the catering table looked over at us.

"Olivia! Keep it down!" I said to her and grabbed her arm. "People are looking at you."

"No more tequila for her," Cassandra informed the caterer. She took Olivia's arm and led her away from the table. "Let's find some coffee."

"I haven't had but two tequilas. I'm fine!" Olivia said brushing Cassandra's hand off her arm. "I am hungry, though!"

"I saw a coffee bar set up over in the far gallery," Sarah suggested.

"Lead the way!" I told her and we followed Sarah into one of the smaller gallery rooms.

"A-ME-LI-A! Amelia Spencer!" A high pitched voice called out.

I turned and saw Holly Smith running across the gallery. She tripped slightly, but steadied herself and made her way to embrace me with a big bear hug.

"Holly! I am so surprised to see you," I told her.

"You knew I wouldn't miss our reunion! Will you be here for the big Rice game tomorrow?" she asked.

"Yes, we will. Holly, let me introduce my good friends from Dogwood Cove: Cassandra Reynolds, Olivia Rivers and Sarah McCaffrey," I announced.

"Nice to meet all of you," she said with an exuberant smile.

Holly Smith was our former Gamma Phi Beta President. She was a real "go getter" and was border-line pesky at times. She loved all things Gamma Phi, and, under her leadership, our sorority had grown into one of the largest chapters in the Southwest.

"I must insist you all stop by the house tomorrow morning for a pre-game sorority brunch. The girls would love to have you and all of our alumnae will be attendance," she demanded and looked at us expectantly.

That was just great. Katherine had been in my pledge class. I hoped she would be too busy to come.

"Of course, Katherine will be there! We can't have our most famous sister in town and not have her to the house! The girls are so excited to meet her!" she bounced up and down and looked as if she were going to try a hurky cheerleading jump. That was Holly — so full of spirit.

"I'll try to make it," I smiled and attempted to change the subject. "Have you seen Leslie Lane tonight, Holly? She's here and sounds like she's going to be filming a movie soon!"

"Really? I've got to go find her and invite her to the brunch. Tootles!" Holly shouted over her shoulder.

"Tootles! Tah, tah!" Olivia called out after her. "Is she oblivious to everything and everyone?" Olivia observed.

"No, she's just a former sorority girl who still thinks she's in the middle of rush!" I replied and chortled. Rush is when the sororities compete for the incoming freshmen girls. Everything from grades to recommendations from former sorority sisters is reviewed. SMU had a very competitive Greek system. At one time, sixty-seven percent of the student body was a member of a sorority or fraternity.

"You wouldn't catch me joining a sorority," Olivia assured me. "I wouldn't want to pay to belong to a clique."

"You do have a way with words, Olivia," Cassandra observed. "I'll have you know I was a Tri-Delta."

"I should have guessed! That explains a lot!" Olivia snorted and poked Cassandra in the ribs.

"Are you going to go tomorrow?" Sarah asked. "I would. I wouldn't let the likes of Katherine Gold keep me from enjoying myself!"

"Truer words have never been spoken," Cassandra agreed.

"We'll see. I'll sleep on it," I told them.

We stood around the coffee bar, ordering our espresso and cappuccinos. Olivia helped herself to the chocolate covered espresso beans.

"Watch it!" Cassandra warned her. "You'll be up all night!"

"Thank you for the warning, Mom," Olivia replied.

As we were turning around to find a seat, we ran smack into the praying mantis herself and her assistant.

"Well, if it isn't little Miss Amelia Spencer from Poe-dunk Cove, Tennessee!" Katherine said as she sneered and looked me over from head to toe. "I can't believe you found anything to wear for something this sophisticated. Oh, but I forgot, you do have a Walmart in 'Hickville.' They do have a nice formalwear section," she gloated.

"Shane was right when he said you were a real witch!" Cassandra said standing toe to toe with Katherine. "I've heard stories about you around Hollywood, and if half of what they say is true, your career is a total wash up! I heard your contract with 'The Rich and The Lost' is not being renewed," Cassandra scoffed.

Katherine looked shocked. Her mouth hung open and she was momentarily speechless. Cassandra had hit a nerve. That didn't stop her for long.

"Speaking of Shane, where is he?" Katherine pantomimed looking around the room for someone. "Let me guess — you couldn't hold on to him too," Katherine snapped.

"Ladies, ladies, let's keep this down," the pinstriped suit pleaded with us. "We don't want any of this discussion becoming tomorrow's headlines," Katherine's assistant emphasized.

"Then tell 'Miss Femme Fatale' to apologize to my friend," Cassandra demanded. I had never seen her so angry before.

"Apologize for what?" Katherine spat. "Apologize for saving her from that boring boyfriend of hers? She's better off. He was like clay in my capable hands," she bragged and smiled, looking at me to see if she had inflicted pain.

"Katherine. That's enough!" Jett roared at her. "Get a grip and have some decency about yourself."

With all the chaos going on, I had not seen Jett approach the coffee bar. By now, all the caterers and servers were standing around gawking. This had turned into a big scene and one I wasn't sure how to exit from.

"Oh, how classic!" Katherine hissed. " 'Dudley-Do-Right' arrives to save the damsel in distress. She always had her friends rescuing her!"

It was then that I realized Olivia had been right. Katherine was not happy, not really. She may have had fame, a beautiful body, and money, but she was not happy. One can have all that and still feel all alone. And from the way she was behaving, I couldn't see her maintaining relationships with anyone. I think that's why she tried to steal other people's happiness. She was a miserable person.

"Katherine, let's go. You've said enough for one night!" the suit chided her. "Please excuse us."

As the assistant rushed Katherine out the door, the photographers were busily snapping pictures of her hasty retreat. We were all left standing, shell shocked, at what had just taken place.

Leslie approached our group and put her arm around me. "Don't fret. That's as bad as she gets. All bark and no bite."

"Cassandra, is it true what you said about her contract not being up for renewal?" I asked. If it were true, Katherine would be devastated. She had landed the job straight out of SMU. It was all she had been doing the past twenty years.

"It's true," Cassandra answered. "Ratings are down and budgets are being slashed. Katherine is a high salaried soap star." I had forgotten Cassandra was a friend with the Bowman's who had created, directed and produced "The Rich and The Lost."

"And now she's a former soap queen who's too old to do much of anything else. She's typecast," Leslie predicted.

"Well, if her assistant was worried about tomorrow's headlines, maybe she should have had a talk with her star about behaving herself," Olivia added.

"Her assistant is her sister, Monica Gold," Leslie said to the group.

"That was Monica?" I asked in disbelief. "The last time I saw her she was getting ready to graduate from high school. She used to come and visit from time to time on the weekends."

"I don't envy her working with Katherine," Sarah empathized. "That would be a miserable existence for me," she stated.

"Well, I don't know about all of you," Olivia said addressing the group, "But I could go for a steak about now. Is there a good place nearby?"

"I've got a great idea. Leslie, join us!" I excused myself and made a call to Dakota's, a chic downtown Dallas spot located eighteen feet underground. The ride down the elevator was worth a trip there just to see the waterfalls. The restaurant had an interesting history. Since it was built on the First Baptist Dallas Church property, it had a legally binding clause that no alcohol could be served on the premises. In order to serve wine and alcohol, the owners decided to go one block below street level to build Dakota's. They had a table for five available and would hold it for us.

"Good night, Jett," I told him. "Thanks for interceding on my behalf, but I don't need you to. You don't owe me a thing."

"Amelia. I'm sorry. I'm sorry for everything. If I could go back in time, I would change it all," he said. He looked sad and so sincere.

"Look, you wouldn't be with Laura and those beautiful babies, and I wouldn't have my family. It was meant to be. No regrets. I want you to know how happy I am and happy with my life in Dogwood Cove. I can't imagine living any other way," I reassured him.

"I'm glad to hear it and glad you have such good friends," he said smiling around at the girls standing around us. "I feel better knowing everything turned out well for you."

"Be happy," I told him and turned and walked out the museum.

Chapter Eight

"Have you seen the headlines this morning?" Sarah asked as she shook me awake. "You need to read this."

"Hmm. What time is it? My alarm hasn't gone off yet," I pleaded and yawned. I sat up in bed. "What's so important that it can't wait for coffee or at least a strong pot of Irish breakfast tea?"

"It's Katherine Gold. She's *The Dallas Morning News* headline," Sarah informed me.

What now? Hadn't last night been enough?

Sarah handed me the front page of the paper. "SMU Grad is Good as Gold" was the headline. A full color half page picture of Katherine posing at the entrance of Meadows Museum was the lead story.

"Well, she's lucky no reporters overheard the argument last night with Cassandra. If the details of her contract negotiations leaked out, there would definitely be a different headline," I said sleepily.

"Her sister made certain there was no negative press, I'm sure," Sarah said and nodded her head confidently. "She will make sure she spins everything in the best light."

"I'll read it after I have a cup of coffee," I told her and headed for the bathroom.

"Don't bother!" Olivia said and plopped herself down on the bed. "It's a bunch of horse hockey about how successful Katherine is, how she is the highest paid soap opera actress and her latest torrid love affair with her 'boy toy,' Conrad Ryan. There's even a quote about how she is receiving the "Distinguished Alumni Award" at half time at the game today. I think I'm going to toss my cookies," Olivia groaned.

"Well, from what Cassandra says, this may be her last hooray. Let her have it," I said, quite honestly. I moved into the bathroom.

After showering and dressing for the homecoming festivities, I joined the girls in the living room. Cassandra was on the phone and Olivia and Sarah were waiting on me at the sofa.

Sarah was wearing a red and blue varsity-style sweater and rolled up blue jeans for today's game against Rice. A pair of saddle oxfords and color coordinated bobby socks and she was ready for a sock-hop!

Olivia went with her traditional Wranglers, red boots, embroidered turquoise shirt and red cowgirl hat. Her Santa Fe style silver belt buckle was studded with pieces of turquoise. She looked the part of a true cowgirl.

Cassandra hung up the phone and joined us. "That was my friend, Melissa Bowman, producer of 'The Rich and the Lost,'" she revealed. "She confirmed that Katherine has been let go from the show. Her last episode airs in two weeks. Apparently, she is considering relocating to Dallas. She's been sending out demos to the local television stations to do a show similar to *Entertainment Tonight* but based in Dallas. It will be called *The Talk of Texas*," Cassandra informed us.

"No wonder Monica is being so careful about the press out here," Olivia inferred. "SMU Grad Makes Gold." That will get her into the right country clubs and job opportunities.

"Amelia, you need to read the article," Sarah said handing me the paper. "She has managed to make herself out to be the girl next door who became famous. She is a mixture of Mother Teresa meets Christy Brinkley. She really has done a great job of creating a phony history."

"It will catch up with her eventually," Cassandra said. She was dressed today in a chic tan suede skirt, matching boots and belted long sleeved cobalt blue shirt. She was wearing a "Go Mustangs" pen. Cassandra didn't wear jeans unless she was camping. And SMU games were notoriously known to be a dressy affair.

"I am looking forward to showing you ladies around campus and attending the game," I told them. "I think Katherine will be so busy with her spin doctors and paparazzi that we will probably not see her." *Well, that was what I was hoping at least,* I thought to myself.

After last night, I was quickly reminded at how ugly she could be. Her insulting comments and the need to inflict pain took me back twenty years to our days on campus. It wasn't enough for her that every guy practically stumbled over his own feet to turn and watch her walk by. She had to have every man's attention. There were more arguments over at the Gamma Phi Beta house after mixers with the fraternities regarding Katherine's behavior. I wasn't the only one who had lost her beau to Katherine over the years.

I had been a good friend to her. I was always defending that friendship during the sorority functions when the other girls were upset with all the attention she was getting from their dates.

"Oh, you know Katherine is just a flirt," I would placate them. "She doesn't even realize what she's doing. She would never hurt a friend!"

I had been so stupid! I should have called "a spade a spade" and let her deal with the fall out. I had been protecting her and had actually enabled her poor behavior. I was part of the problem. Now her sister, Monica, was taking up where I had left off.

Talking with Jett last night had brought closure. I wasn't thinking about it, but it had never been resolved. His apology, though slightly overdue, needed to be said. Knowing that he had regrets about his involvement with Katherine helped me to move on. I would never again look back at my years at SMU with a knot in my stomach. I was no longer a victim. I felt suddenly empowered. That naive girl from Dogwood Cove had been replaced with a confident woman!

Carl was waiting at the entrance of the hotel. A short drive later with some directions to Sorority Row, we were standing in front of the Gamma Phi Beta house with its massive white columns and Georgian architecture. Homecoming banners and welcome signs were draped across the front of the house.

"Gosh, this looks more like a mansion than a sorority house!" Olivia said.

"You're right," Sarah agreed. "I had no idea sorority houses were this nice."

We walked into the front entry and were greeted by the current Gamma Phi girls. They showed us into the dining room which had been set up with a long buffet.

"Oh, my gosh!" Olivia cried. "They have ranchos huevos!" This tex-mex breakfast dish is made with corn tortillas, eggs, salsa, refried beans and jalapenos. It is a Texas staple. "I'm happy as a clam!" she exclaimed.

"Help yourselves, Ladies!" Holly called out to us. She had on her Gamma Phi Beta colors of pink and brown and recruiting attitude. "It's so good to see you this morning. Amelia, did you see *The Dallas Morning News* today? Your former roommate is once again in the headlines. We are hoping the reporters will cover her visit here this morning as well," Holly gushed and smiled her enthusiastic trademark grin.

"Oh, great! A visit from 'Cruella DeVille!' " Olivia muttered under her breath.

"Leslie Lane! Welcome, welcome!" Holly sang out!

"Hello, ladies," Leslie waved at us. "May I join you this morning?"

"Absolutely," Cassandra said and pulled out a chair.

"Miss Lane! I am a huge fan. May I have your autograph?" a doe eyed college aged girl asked her politely.

"Of course. To whom should I make this out?" Leslie asked her.

She signed several autographs while she was at the house. *Wicked* was a very popular show and several of the Gamma Phi's had gone on a trip to New York and met Leslie backstage after her performance. She was very humble and always took time for her fans.

Holly went around the dining room handing out pledge promises to each of the alumnae. "Mrs. Reynolds," she said, "We would be pleased if you considered a one-time gift to the Gamma Phi Beta foundation. It inspires leadership skills in young women and also goes towards our charity summer camps for underprivileged children."

"Thank you, Holly. I will look over this and mail it back to you," Cassandra said and smiled.

"Amelia, have you made out your will and bequeathed your gift to Gamma Phi?" Holly inquired.

I swallowed hard and looked up at Holly. "Ahh, that's something Shane and I will be discussing, privately," I cautioned her.

"Well, I'll give you a call and follow up with that after the reunion!" Holly chirped and moved on to the next table of alumnae in attendance.

"Is she the 'Grim Reaper' or what?" Olivia asked in total shock. "It's not enough to come right out and ask Cassandra for money, but to point blank ask Amelia about her will is a little weird to me," she crossed her arms and pushed her plate away. She abruptly announced, "I'm ready to go!"

I had to agree with Olivia. I was ready to go to and that was a bit pushy. Holly had always been that way, Gamma Phi first. She would always be promoting Gamma Phi. I suddenly wondered what her personal life was like. I had not asked her at the cocktail party. All we had talked about was Gamma Phi and its most famous alumnae, Katherine Gold.

"Let's hurry up and eat and head for the homecoming parade," I instructed the girls. "We don't need a repeat of last night."

"Before you go, you girls will need a pass for the VIP skybox," Holly said handing each of us a blue pass with a red mustang on the front. "We can't have someone as important as Cassandra Reynolds sitting in the general seating section!"

Olivia rolled her eyes and Cassandra kicked her under the table.

"Thank you, Holly. This is very generous of you," Cassandra responded courteously.

"Leslie, will you join us for the homecoming parade?" I asked her.

"Thanks, but I am singing the National Anthem before the kick off. I have to go to the game early, but how about meeting in the skybox later," she suggested.

"That would be great!" I hugged her and we were off for the parade. The sidewalks were beginning to fill with underclassmen dressed in Harvard crimson and Yale blue, our school's colors, to symbolize SMU's high academic standards. As the police escorts began the parade, the Mustang mascot named Peruna, walked and shook hands with small children along the parade route.

The school mascot became the Mustangs when a past president's assistant commented that the football team looked like "a bunch of wild mustangs" out on the field. The student body adopted the symbol and gave the Mustang the nickname Peruna after a patented tonic with a "high alcoholic kick to it." It is rumored that Ford named their car model after the SMU mustang football team.

"Oh, look girls!" Olivia squealed. Two men had a halter around a small, black Shetland pony with hooves painted red and blue. The pony had been a symbol of the school since 1932.

The SMU marching band was next in the parade route. Their red and white candy striped jackets with white pants, white gloves and straw top hats earned them the nickname "The

Best Dressed Band in the Land." They were a true jazz and swing performance band and played loud and proud.

"They are awesome!" Cassandra shouted. "I've never heard anything like them."

"They are the only true jazz marching band in the country," I told her.

"I love jazz and swing," Sarah interjected over the loud music.

We were having a wonderful time watching each of the floats pass with co-eds on board throwing candy to the crowd. Each sorority had partnered with a fraternity to build a float. This year's theme was "Rolling Out The Red Carpet." One sorority had built a miniature version of Tara since their theme was *Gone With the Wind*. Scarlett O'Hara attired in her Twelve Oaks picnic dress and straw hat stood on the front porch with Rhett Butler, and waved at the crowd.

"I love it!" I shouted, jumping up and down, clapping my hands in time with our fight song.

"Oh, my gosh!" Sarah gasped! "Isn't that Katherine?"

It sure was. Riding on the top of the back seat in a convertible gold Ford mustang was Katherine. A banner across both sides of the car read "Katherine Gold, Distinguished Alumnus and Homecoming Queen, Class of 1990"

"Oh, PLEASE!" Olivia sneered with sarcasm in her voice. "She looks so ridiculous!"

The mustang stopped and Katherine stood up in the back seat, alternating kisses to the applauding crowd and doing her best rendition of a Miss America cat walk wave. She showed off her dark spray tan in a gold sequin pageant gown. She was wearing elbow length white satin gloves and waving wildly to the crowd.

Katherine could be heard crying, "I love you all! I love you all!" The crowd was applauding wildly. More than one man in the crowd received an elbowing in the ribs from their wives who didn't seem to appreciate how their husbands were gawking at her.

The parade continued down Hill Crest Avenue.

"I've got to stop at Bubba's for a chicken biscuit," Olivia shouted to us and headed towards the famous chicken hang out. "I've heard about this place on *Diners, Drive-Ins and Dives* on the Food Network."

"We'll wait for you here and then head over to Bishop's Boulevard for all the pre-game festivities," I yelled to her over the roar of the crowd.

Olivia soon returned with a bag full of chicken biscuits for all of us.

"We just ate!" Cassandra reminded her.

"I don't define swallowing food as fast as you can to hurry and get away from the 'Grim Reaper' at the Gamma Phi Beta house, as eating," Olivia told her. "I didn't even have time to take the edge off my appetite."

"Olivia, you are going to have to end up with a farmer to keep you supplied in food day in and day out," Cassandra observed. "I've never seen anyone eat so much and still be so tiny."

"I pull my own weight," Olivia challenged. "I would like to see most men try to even keep up with me!"

We carefully crossed Hill Crest Avenue and headed towards Bishop Boulevard. Everywhere you looked there were red and blue tents with students handing out plates full of BBQ, cocktails, hamburgers and hotdogs.

"This is definitely different than a University of Tennessee tail gate party," Sarah said.

"Well, UT has the capacity to hold slightly over one hundred two thousand. This stadium seats a little over thirty-four thousand," I quickly told her. "SMU is a much smaller campus."

"Instead of *Rocky Top*, they play sophisticated jazz tunes," Olivia said with a trace of irony in her voice. "This is how the Ivy League elite tail gates. Bartenders and jazz."

"Well, I love pregame parties in Knoxville, especially the Vol Navy!" Sarah said.

That was the name given to the house boats and yachts that navigated down the Tennessee River and tied together the Friday before every UT home game. Fans would BBQ, party and whoop it up. It was an all weekend event.

"This is definitely different from a UT game day, but I like it," Cassandra said. Reynolds's Candies was a corporate supporter of UT athletics. Her blood ran orange. Doug was also a graduate of the University of Tennessee. They were both strongly involved in the alumni association of the school.

We all decided that the homecoming festivities were top-notch at SMU. Some tents sported bartenders who mixed wonderful pregame concoctions. Others served Texas style mesquite wood smoked BBQ and ranch beans, very different from the sweet brown sugar and molasses beans we ate in Tennessee. It was all wonderful and tasty!

I showed the girls around campus, and we sat around the fountain outside Dallas Hall and enjoyed the clear blue fall sky that had decided to grace the day. It was one of those picture perfect moments with good friends, beautiful weather, and fun festivities. Little did I know that our picture perfect moment would be so short lived!

Chapter Nine

I was so excited to attend my first game in the new Gerald J. Ford Stadium on campus. We walked past the Doak Walker Plaza, in honor of SMU's most famous football player and Heisman Trophy winner. There was also a monument to a fallen Peruna mascot.

"This is so much fun!" Sarah said wide eyed with excitement. "I love game day festivities."

"Tickets please," a tall gentleman said as he extended his hand.

"Could you please direct us to the VIP skybox?" I politely asked him.

"Right this way, m'am," he said. He radioed for an escort and we were taken upstairs to the upper level deck to a beautifully decorated lounge with a wonderful view of the entire football field.

"So this is how the rich and famous live," Olivia observed. "I think I could get used to this." She was smiling and really enjoying herself today.

We watched as the Rice players wearing their navy jerseys began warming up on the field. Soon after, the SMU cheerleaders made a tunnel on the field for their players to run through. The fans began screaming!

"May I get you ladies something to drink today?" a young lady in black pants and a white tuxedo shirt asked us. We placed our orders with her and began exploring the posh skybox.

"Do you get to sit in the skybox for all the UT games?" Sarah asked Cassandra.

"Sometimes," she responded. "I prefer sitting in our regular assigned tickets because the excitement of the crowd is so contagious."

The SMU jazz band began making a formation on the playing field, preparing for the National Anthem. The Honor Guard filed on the field bearing the American flag in the center, the Texas State flag on the right and the SMU school flag on the left.

Leslie walked up to the microphone and paused. She looked stunning in a beautiful red suit, her long black hair in stark contrast.

"Now Ladies and Gentlemen, we are proud to have one of our alumni joining us today, representing the class of 1990 and star of the Broadway show, *Wicked*, our very own Leslie Lane!" The announcer's voice boomed.

As the band struck the first note, Leslie began singing one of the most beautiful renditions I had ever heard of *The Star Spangled Banner*. Her trained voice sang out clearly as she hit the last note. The crowd's loud applause was all the acknowledgment she needed.

"Her former music professors must be so proud of her," Sarah leaned towards me and yelled over the crowd. "She is marvelous!"

"She really is!" I said, beaming with pride at my old room mate who was finally making it. I remember the countless hours Leslie used to sing scales in our rental house and stretch on a make-shift ballet barre she installed in our living room. The hours she practiced point was a show of her commitment to her art.

"I really hope she gets the part in Ron Howard's movie. She is very deserving. She has paid her dues in New York. It's on to the big time for her," Cassandra stated, wiping the tears from her eyes, touched by Leslie's beautiful performance.

"I hope so too," I told her and gave her a hug. I was so proud of Leslie.

"There she is now!" Sarah squealed, bouncing a little.

"Congratulations, Leslie," I said hugging her. "That was incredible! Your voice gets better all the time."

"Oh, thank you Amelia. You are too sweet," Leslie said, blushing.

"She's just speaking the truth," Olivia went over to her and shook her hand. "I feel like I'm in the presence of greatness, Leslie."

Wow, I had not heard Olivia show so much praise to anyone before. She was definitely moved by Leslie's performance. Music can have that affect on people.

"Let's get some champagne for Ms. Lane and toast her impending success in Hollywood," Cassandra said and motioned to the young lady waiting on us.

"Right away," the server said. She soon returned with a silver tray and five champagne flutes filled with bubbly.

"To Leslie Lane!" we toasted and clanked our glasses.

"And to 'The Traveling Tea Ladies!' " I added.

" 'Traveling Tea Ladies?' " Leslie questioned. "Oh, I get the connection with Amelia and the tea. That sounds like fun! I want to be one," she laughed.

"Today, we add a new member to our group," I said and gave Leslie a hug. We were so glad to be sharing our homecoming weekend with her.

Remind me to give you some autographed playbills and posters from *Wicked.* I brought them with me for you to take home to give Emma and Charlie.

"Oh Leslie, you are so thoughtful. They will love them!"

"I hate to interrupt your little love fest!" Katherine cut in with a big grin on her face, her teeth in an insincere smile, edge-to-edge. "You two were always so sweet to each other," she continued with her saccharin grin.

I had not heard Katherine walk up behind us. She strutted into the skybox, still wearing her sash and gold sequin dress.

"Did your face move when you said that or have you had one too many Botox injections?" Olivia shot back at her.

"Liv, back down," I murmured to her. "Let's not make a scene."

"Yes, let's not make a scene, Annie Oakley! She quipped stepping back and looking up and down at Olivia's boots and belt. This skybox is not big enough for the two of us," she sneered at Olivia.

"Well, it just goes to show you that will let just anybody in here these days," Cassandra said and shot a nasty glance at Katherine.

"Katherine! Please! Behave!" Monica pleaded with her.

"Oh, these two were always so jealous of me, Monica, jealous of my looks, jealous that I was more popular, jealous that I got the lead in the spring production, jealous that I ended up with their boyfriends!" Katherine snarled.

Leslie lost her temper at this point. "Katherine, I am so tired of you thinking the world and everyone in it revolves around you. You have become such a pathetic and hateful person. The sad thing is that is why you are all alone now. Maybe at one time you had the looks, the prime parts, and the guys. But it is all fading and now you are left with only the person staring back in the mirror. I truly feel sorry for you!" Leslie said hatefully.

Katherine hauled back her hand and slapped Leslie across the face. You could almost hear a pin drop in the skybox as everyone stopped what they were doing to watch the exchange. Leslie was in shock with her mouth open, holding her hand up to her face as a red mark began appearing on her cheek.

"Katherine, come with me. The press would like to get a photo of you with the president of SMU," Monica Gold demanded and grabbed her sister's arm and led her quickly away. She looked over her shoulder with worry and concern written all over her face.

"Leslie, are you all right?" I asked as I examined her cheek. Her eyes had begun tearing up.

"I'm fine. That's the LAST time she will get away with treating me like that again!" Leslie declared.

"M'am. Here's some ice for your face," our server said. We had not realized that the catering staff had also witnessed the exchange.

"Thank you very much," Leslie told her as she placed the ice bag against her cheek. "I am so embarrassed that happened. I shouldn't have said anything, but I just couldn't take anymore of her pompous attitude!"

"Don't worry, Leslie!" Cassandra reassured her. "I'm sure no one even noticed."

"I think she needs a can of whoop 'you know what' opened up on her!" Olivia threatened. "She called me Annie Oakley! Who even thinks to say things like that?" she wondered out loud.

"I would take it as a supreme compliment," I reassured Olivia and rubbed her arm. I felt so bad that Katherine had managed to ruin our homecoming festivities. Whatever possessed her to be so mean and hurtful? I suddenly felt bad for Monica trying to contain all her sister's hate that seemed to ooze from every pore of Katherine's body!

"Poor Monica," I told the girls. "She was a nice kid. I hate to see that she spends her time managing her sister's career. It can't be an easy job for her."

They all shook their heads in agreement.

I remember Monica as very quiet, shy and sweet. The few weekends she visited Katherine, she stayed at the house and we popped pop corn, watched movies and listened to music. She was a rather serious girl and the complete opposite of her sister. I couldn't imagine spending all day cleaning up after Katherine and her messes!

Monica managed to keep Katherine busy with interviews, autographs, and photos with the press. Half-time was soon approaching and Katherine was led away to the football field to be presented with the "Distinguished Alumnus Award."

We watched from the press box as the SMU band performed a rowdy rendition of *She'll Be Coming 'Round the Mountain* and a selection of Jazz standards. They made a center row in their formation for the homecoming court to walk across the field and we watched as the new homecoming King and Queen were crowned. It brought back old memories of my former days on campus.

"And now . . . ladies, gentlemen, and university guests," the announcer's voiced boom on the P.A. system, "Please welcome the President of Southern Methodist University, R. Gerald Turner, as he presents this year's 'Distinguished Alumnus Award!'"

The crowd roared, the color guard stood still at attention, and all eyes were on the field as President Turner walked to the podium.

"We are very privileged today to bestow the award of 'Distinguished Alumnus' to one of our graduates who has achieved great distinction as an award winning actress, winning five Daytime Emmys during her career. We are proud to call her an ambassador of our school and today we honor one of our own. She won the title of Homecoming Queen in 1990 and won all of our hearts. We are very proud today to have her home once again to take the walk to center field, escorted by Peruna to receive her award. Please help me welcome, Miss Katherine Gold!" President Turner said and began clapping enthusiastically.

We watched from the skybox as Katherine took the arm of the costumed Mustang mascot who was wearing blue and red tails for the occasion. She was smiling as President Turner approached her. She bowed her head as he took a rather large tiara from a nearby pillow on the podium and placed it carefully on Katherine's head. The tiara bobbled a bit and Katherine grabbed it before it slid off her head and affixed the side combs firmly to prevent any further slipping.

Katherine beamed her beautiful trademark smile to the crowd and began waving to the onlookers who by now were on their feet applauding.

"This looks like a bad rendition of *Carrie*," Olivia whispered in my ear.

"I didn't know that they gave a tiara for 'Distinguished Alumnus Awards,'" Cassandra said with her arms crossed.

"I didn't know they made tiaras that BIG!" Sarah said, her eyes widening.

"That was Katherine's idea," Holly announced standing behind us. "She wanted to make a big production of it!" She was smiling and clapping as Katherine began walking across the field.

"She startled me," Sarah admitted. "Does Holly always sneak up on you like that?" she complained.

Katherine paced the field, walking from the center line to the end zone and back to the center, waving wildly at the crowd. The fans whistled and clapped loudly as she continued her Miss America catwalk strut. She took her time, stretching out the moment. The autumn sun reflected off her gold sequin dress and cast a gold light on her heavily made up face. Her sash fluttered in the breeze and she grabbed it and straightened it several times. She turned at the center line and began walking to work the crowd on the opposite end of the field. She blew kisses to her fans and mouthed the words "I love you" over and over again.

"Oh, get on with this already," Olivia murmured. "This reminds me of a flashback to my childhood when my sister forced me to play with beauty pageant Barbie. I would much rather be horseback riding right now," she groaned.

"She's really milking the crowd," Cassandra observed. "I'm not sure I could have walked the entire field in those gold stilettos without breaking off a heel."

The jazz band continued playing *She'll Be Coming Round the Mountain* and changing formations on the field. They maneuvered so they made two lines on either side of Katherine for her grand exit from Ford Stadium. The crowd still stood on their feet and clapped to the beat.

Just then, Katherine stopped in mid-strut. She paused as the crowd continued to clap in unison.

Is she coming back for another trip around the field? I wondered to myself.

The crowd didn't seem to mind if she did. The applause got wilder and more frantic. "Katherine, Katherine, Katherine . . . " they began chanting.

She pivoted and began making her way back towards the side lines. Just then, she fell to her knees as if in slow motion, her eyes wide with shock. She grasped her throat with both hands, apparently struggling to get air.

A gasp went up through the crowd as we all watched in disbelief as she sank onto the grassy field.

"Oh, my gosh! What is wrong with Katherine?" Leslie screamed and grabbed my hand.

Katherine was now sprawled on her back as President Turner signaled for the paramedics from the sidelines. Katherine was motionless, her face turning blue, and her tiara lay next to her body. Monica Gold quickly ran out onto the field and kneeled down next to her sister.

A sickening hush fell across the crowded stadium as everyone watched the scene unfold in horror. The medics had begun CPR and were administering chest compressions and oxygen. A waiting gurney was rolled onto the field. We watched as she was quickly placed on it and rushed to a waiting ambulance, the paramedics continuing CPR as they loaded her into the ambulance at the end zone. Monica was assisted into the vehicle by several police officers and the doors slammed shut behind her.

As the ambulance pulled away with lights and sirens blaring, a murmur rose up around the stadium. Small children were being consoled by their parents, cheerleaders and band members were seen hugging each other in disbelief. What had happened?

Leslie and I put our arms around each other, unable to speak. The announcer came back over the intercom and told the sold out crowd that there would be a slight delay in the second half of the game and thanked us for our patience.

I couldn't believe what was going on. It all seemed like a bad dream. Olivia was right! It was something like a bad rendition of *Carrie*. What had happened to Katherine?

Chapter Ten

"I still can't believe it" Cassandra commented.

We were all sitting in the living room of our suite, still in shock the next morning. A copy of *The Dallas Morning News* was on the coffee table in front of us. The headline read, "Katherine Gold Dies at College Homecoming Game." The article had pictures of fans crying and a temporary memorial of flowers being placed outside of Ford Stadium. Quotes from her shocked co-stars from the "Rich and the Lost" were in the paper as well as from the executive directors, the Bowmans.

"It says in the paper that it appears she suffered a heart attack," Sarah said blowing her nose. "As much as I didn't care for her, I feel so sorry that it happened in front of an entire crowd of people," she lamented.

"How are you holding up, Amelia?" Olivia inquired. I had hardly slept at all and had spent a few hours crying on the phone with Shane. It truly was a tragedy.

"I still can't believe it," I replied. I was still wearing my robe and slippers. We had decided to order breakfast in the room and were staying up to date with news reports. "I just feel like I can hardly catch my breath," I added.

"Here, sit down, Amelia," Sarah said and patted the couch. "You need some coffee and maybe a strong shot of whiskey to settle your nerves," she suggested.

"I'll take some coffee for now," I conceded and smiled at Cassandra. My eyes looked like swollen slits and my face was splotchy. "As much as detested Katherine's behavior, I still loved her. She was part of my history," I told the girls.

Just then a news update appeared on the television. "This just is just in from the Greater Dallas Metropolitan Coroner's Office: an autopsy has been ordered in the death of Miss Katherine Gold, former Emmy winning soap opera actress best known for her role on 'The Rich and The Lost.' She suffered an apparent heart attack at the half-time show of the SMU homecoming game yesterday. She was pronounced dead at the arrival of Medical City Dallas. Police have not ruled out foul play," the reporter said a bit stoically.

The screen showed the Chief of Police, Bob Whittaker, speaking to a throng of reporters with microphones swarming outside of the Dallas police headquarters. The chief made a brief statement and did not take any questions from the inquiring paparazzi.

"At this time, we cannot rule out foul play in the death of Miss Gold yesterday. Until a determination is made by the coroner's office, we will proceed to handle this investigation as a homicide. There will be no questions taken at this time. We would appreciate anyone with information to please contact the police department immediately," Chief Whittaker said.

"We now return to our regularly scheduled programming already in progress," the news anchor announced.

"Foul play?" Olivia asked bewildered. "I don't know what they think they are going to find out from her autopsy. It looked to me like she collapsed from a heart attack," she concluded.

"I wonder why they are treating this like a homicide investigation?" I asked aloud. "They must have some reason to think it wasn't a heart attack."

"Maybe because she was a celebrity and they are giving the investigation the star treatment. You saw all the paparazzi. This story is as big as they get!" Cassandra interjected. Just then her cell phone rang. She excused herself and went out to the terrace to take the call.

When she came back in her face was white.

"What's wrong, Cassandra?" I asked as I jumped up from the sofa. Cassandra held both my shoulders and looked straight into my eyes.

"I just got off the phone with my friends at 'The Rich and The Lost.' Needless to say they are all in shock. Katherine had already filmed her final scenes and finished production. Of course, the public doesn't know about her contract not being renewed," she told us, paused and took a deep breath.

"Amelia, the Dallas police have been asking if anyone had a motive to kill Katherine. She had been receiving death threats through the mail. Monica had tried to cover it up, but the producers had contacted the FBI because the letters became increasingly hostile," Cassandra continued.

"Who would want to hurt Katherine?" I asked as I shook my head in disbelief.

"Well, I for one wanted to toss her around by her hair. She tends to have that affect on people!" Olivia said standing with her hands on her hips.

"Shush your mouth, Olivia!" Sarah whispered very seriously. "You shouldn't speak ill of the dead," she warned.

"All I am saying, Sarah, is that I can see she didn't have a lot of fans if this weekend was any indication of how she behaved most of the time," Olivia retorted. She was getting irritated.

"She has a HUGE fan base now!" Cassandra said. "You can't turn on a television without them running a story on Katherine. And 'The Rich and The Lost' is running a marathon of Katherine's story line over the years. The public is clamoring for everything they can get their hands on about Katherine," she concluded.

It is rather strange how when an actor or entertainer tragically dies or dies unexpectedly, that the public can become crazed and lift them up to a "demi-god" stature. It had happened with Elvis, Marilyn Monroe and more recently with Anna Nicole Smith and Michael Jackson. Add the name Katherine Gold to the list. Every gossip magazine and entertainment news show had her death as the headline. She was much more famous dead than alive.

Ironically she was being martyred as the sweet and innocent "girl next door" who made it big. Every celebrity that was interviewed had some wonderful story to share about Katherine.

Just then our hotel phone rang, startling all of us. Sarah hurried over to answer the phone.

"Hello," Sarah snapped.

"Mrs. Spencer, please," A male voice asked abruptly with a slight Texas twang.

"Just one moment. Amelia, it's for you," Sarah said and handed me the phone.

"This is Amelia Spencer," I stated.

"Mrs. Spencer, this is Detective Matt Lincoln of the Dallas Metropolitan Police Department. Would it be possible for you to come to the station to help in our investigation of the Katherine Gold case?" Detective Lincoln requested.

"I don't understand. I'd be happy to help in any way I can, but I don't see how I can shed any light on the investigation," I told him.

"Well I understand that you were Miss Gold's college roommate as was a Miss Leslie Lane," Detective Lincoln remarked.

"Yes, I was but I had not see Katherine in twenty years," I reminded him.

"You may be able to provide some details that will point us in the right direction. By the way, do you have any idea how to reach Miss Lane? We would like her to come to the station as well," he added.

My mind began whirring as I tried to fathom why the detective would want to speak to both Leslie and myself. Were we under suspicion?

"I can call Leslie's cell phone and ask her to meet us. I believe she is still in town," I told Detective Lincoln.

"When can I expect you?" he urged.

"I will get there as soon as I can. Thank you," I said and hung up.

"Who was that, Amelia?" Olivia asked with a puzzled look on her face.

"I think Amelia may need a lawyer," Cassandra announced.

"Oh, I don't think so!" I quickly spoke up. "The detective wants Leslie and I to come in and answer some questions about Katherine."

"What kind of questions?" Olivia asked. "I've watched a lot of *Law and Order* episodes and I think Cassandra is right. You better hire an attorney."

"I don't have anything to do with Katherine's death. I don't have anything to hide. Anything I can do to help the Dallas police, I am willing to do it," I declared. I started to get up and head to the bathroom to shower and change into some clothes.

"Amelia, listen to your friends!" Sarah pleaded. "If for any reason the detective starts to make you feel uncomfortable, you stop talking and ask for a lawyer."

"Ok, ok! I've got to call Leslie and have her meet me at the station," I assured Sarah.

"I will have Carl pick her up on our way," Cassandra said and picked up her cell phone.

"*Our* way?" I challenged her.

"Yes, we are all going!" Olivia pronounced and arched her eyebrow daring me to defy her. I knew better than to argue with a stubborn red head and I really could use the support right now. I was still terribly shaken from Katherine's death.

Cassandra dialed Leslie's number and spoke briefly to her while I showered. Leslie was still in town and was not due to fly out until tomorrow. Cassandra got directions to her hotel and made arrangements for us to pick her up.

An hour later, we were all dressed and riding to Leslie's hotel, a few blocks away. She met us at the front entrance and joined us in the limo.

"Leslie," I said and hugged her. "How are you holding up?"

"Actually, not so good. I still can't believe Katherine's dead," she confessed and dabbed her red nose with a tissue.

"You should think about staying with us tonight," Sarah suggested to her. "We have plenty of room and you shouldn't be alone right now."

"Absolutely!" Olivia agreed.

"I would love to spend more time with you and the girls are right. You shouldn't be alone right now," I implored.

"I think it's a great idea. I will phone your hotel and have Carl pick up your belongings while we are at the station," Cassandra persisted.

"Oh, I don't want to be any trouble," Leslie protested as she shook her head and her eyes filled with tears again.

"No trouble at all!" Cassandra said and leaned forward in her seat. "Carl, will you please swing by Miss Lane's hotel after you drop us off? I would like you to pick up her belongings and take them to our suite at the Adolphus," she requested.

"Yes M'am," Carl answered.

"Now, Leslie. I will tell you what I told Amelia. If for any reason you become uncomfortable with the line of questioning from Detective Lincoln, stop talking and ask for a lawyer. I have our attorney from Reynolds's already on his way," Cassandra resumed.

"Cassandra, why did you do that?" I asked her, immediately taken a back.

"Amelia, they are treating this investigation as a possible homicide. That means they are looking for suspects and I am not going to see my friends implicated in this," Cassandra said running her hands through her hair. She was obviously upset.

"I have also called Shane, and he is flying into Dallas this afternoon. He agreed with me about an attorney," Cassandra declared.

I adamantly asked, "Is that why he hasn't answered his cell phone because he's on a plane?" I couldn't believe it. I didn't know whether to be irritated or glad. Honestly, I really could use his comforting presence right now.

We pulled up in front of police headquarters and approached the front desk.

"Detective Lincoln is expecting us, Amelia Spencer and Leslie Lane," I announced.

"Mrs. Spencer. Miss Lane. I'm Detective Lincoln," a voice announced confidently. A tall muscular man in his mid thirties approached the group. He wore a navy pin striped suit and looked like he stepped from the pages of *Gentlemen's Quarterly Magazine*. He had a strong chiseled chin and offered a wide smile. He shook both of our hands firmly and looked around the group for further introductions.

"Detective Lincoln—these are my friends, Cassandra Reynolds, Sarah McCaffrey and Olivia Rivers," I said making introductions.

"Ladies," he said as he shook their hands and leaned down to make eye contact with each of them.

"Detective Lincoln," Olivia batted her eyes and smiled coyly. "Very nice to meet you."

"Can I get you something to drink while I talk with Mrs. Spencer and Miss Lane?" he asked the threesome.

"Oh, I think we will be fine," Cassandra said, not falling for the smooth talking Texan act.

"Miss Lane, Mrs. Spencer, if you'll follow me," he commanded and led us down the hall way. Olivia, Cassandra and Sarah settled down into very uncomfortable looking chairs in the waiting area while Leslie and I were led down the hall.

He took us into a brightly lit room with a small gray metal table with four matching chairs. The walls were industrial white cinder block. He gestured for us to take a seat. The cold metal chairs gave me a chill and I visibly got goose bumps on my arms.

"Okay," Detective Lincoln instructed and turned on a tape recorder. "I am recording this interview with Mrs. Amelia Spencer and Miss Leslie Lane with your permission, correct?"

"Yes," I stated flatly. I felt like I had a lump in my throat.

"Yes," Leslie agreed.

"How long have you known the deceased, Katherine Gold?" Detective Lincoln asked us as he got out a yellow legal pad and began writing.

"I met Katherine at freshmen orientation in 1986. We were assigned as roommates," I told him.

"Hmm, Yes. And would you say this was an amicable arrangement?" he inquired.

"Yes, I would say so. Yes, very amicable," I responded. I could feel the palms of my hands becoming sweaty.

"And you, Miss Lane. How long have you known Miss Gold?" he continued.

"We met in our first year improvisational class," Leslie remembered looking Detective Lincoln squarely in the eye.

"And when did you become roommates?" he questioned.

"Our junior year. Amelia, Katherine and I rented a small house together," Leslie explained.

"And the three of you were also sorority sisters?" Detective Lincoln acknowledged.

I was beginning to wonder where he was getting his information.

"Yes, yes we were," I agreed and shook my head in the affirmative. I watched him make more notes on his yellow pad.

He began flipping through a file folder sitting on the table. He stopped when he found the document he was looking for.

"Who is Jett Rollins?" he blurted looking for a surprised reaction.

"Why do you want to know about Jett?" Leslie demanded.

"For one, you two were both seen at a cocktail party arguing with the deceased and an argument involved a Mr. Rollins, correct?" He leaned forward, staring me directly in the eye, waiting for my response.

"Jett was my college boyfriend," I admitted. *Why did I feel so nervous*, I wondered?

"Were you two engaged at one time?" he asked point blank.

"I don't see the significance of your question," I protested.

"Just answer the question, Mrs. Spencer. Were you engaged to Mr. Rollins at one time?" Detective Lincoln demanded.

"Yes, we were briefly engaged," I conceded. I could feel the heat rising in my body.

"And who broke off the engagement?" he speculated.

"What does that matter?" Leslie interjected angrily. "They didn't get married. Broken engagements happen all the time!"

"Oh, it matters. It matters very much to this investigation," Detective Lincoln insinuated.

"Amelia. Don't say another word. This interview is over. We would like to speak to our attorney," Leslie countered.

Detective Lincoln spread his hands in a gesture of innocence. "Look ladies. I am simply trying to get the facts straight," he maintained.

"What you are trying to do is imply that a broken engagement from twenty years ago has something to do with Katherine's death," I admonished.

"I'm giving you a chance to clear yourself in this investigation. You were both seen arguing with the deceased the night before her death and again in the skybox just before she walked out on the field. You both have motives for wanting to see Katherine Gold dead," he declared and slammed his pencil down on the legal pad.

"All right. I will cooperate with you. I called off the engagement to Jett," I admitted. I was shaking with anger, incensed with Detective Lincoln.

"What was the reason for ending your engagement?" he asked.

"Amelia, be quiet!" Leslie warned me and grabbed my wrist.

"Leslie, obviously he knows. I want him to hear my side of things," I explained. "I called off the engagement because I found Jett and Katherine in bed together," I divulged. Okay, I hoped he was happy now. I felt totally humiliated.

"And what happened then?" he demanded.

"What do you mean what happened then?" I asked him sarcastically. "I didn't wait around to hear what they had to say. I caught them together and I shut the door and left," I quipped. *Where was he going with this*, I wondered?

"Did you attack Mr. Rollins or Miss Gold when you confronted them?" he speculated.

"No!" I shouted.

"Did you damage Miss Gold's car after leaving the house?" he accused. His questions were becoming more bizarre!

"NO! Absolutely not!" I emphatically stated.

"Did you not flee the country and go to England after finding them in bed together?" he continued. The gloves were off now and I was ready to fight.

"I had plans to leave for England to study abroad. It's just a coincidence I found them together the day before I left," I defended myself.

"And you didn't damage Miss Gold's car that evening before you left Dallas?" he persisted and threw an 8x10 picture of Katherine's car she drove in college on the table. On the side door was spray painted the words, "Die you whore" on the driver's side door. He watched for my reaction.

"I had nothing to do with this!" I reiterated and began shaking.

"Katherine had a lot of enemies," Leslie claimed. "She slept around quite a bit and didn't have a lot of friends as a consequence."

"Where were you the night before Amelia flew to England?" he redirected and turned his attention towards her.

"I was with Amelia at the Gamma Phi Beta House. We were having a going away party for her and we ended up spending the night at the house. I would have to think of who was there, but there were about fifteen of us that night," Leslie recalled.

"Was Holly Smith one of the girls?" he guessed.

So, he had spoken with Holly. No wonder why he had such good background information.

"Holly was there, yes." Leslie recounted.

"Did you know about Miss Gold's car?" he asked me.

"No. I left the next morning from the sorority house and took a taxi to the airport," I insisted.

"And when did you next see Miss Gold?" he snapped.

"The night of the Meadow's Museum cocktail party," I told him tersely.

"You and one of your friends were overheard saying you would have 'tossed her around by her hair,'" He declared as he looked at a document in his file folder.

"Boy, you've really been working overtime on this case, haven't you?" Leslie observed sarcastically. "Anyone who knows Amelia would know that she wouldn't hurt a fly," she continued undaunted by Detective Lincoln's intimidating line of questioning.

"But you would, wouldn't you?" he suddenly flipped on Leslie. "You were involved in an altercation with the deceased at the football game. She actually struck you in the face, correct?" he quoted from his report.

"Yes, she did. That doesn't make me a violent person. That makes HER a violent person," Leslie said defensively.

"And what led up to this exchange between the two of you?" Detective Lincoln quipped.

"You would have to know Katherine to understand how she could antagonize people," Leslie retaliated.

111

"You two were somewhat competitive during your college years, correct?" he prompted Leslie.

"How so?" she snipped back.

"Oh, weren't you two both theatre majors?" Detective Lincoln responded.

"Yes," Leslie replied robotically.

"Didn't she get the lead in the spring production your senior year?" he proceeded.

"Yes, but Leslie won the Bob Hope award," I added. Bob Hope had a special tie with the students of SMU after they playfully kidnapped him and brought him to a pep rally. The theatre on campus was named in his honor.

"Mrs. Spencer. Let Miss Lane answer the question, please," he chastised me and turned back to Leslie.

"Isn't it true that you are auditioning for a part in Ron Howard's next movie?" Lincoln continued.

"Why, yes. How did you know that?" Leslie demanded. I had to give Detective Lincoln an "A" plus for detective work.

"Wasn't Miss Gold also auditioning for the same part?" he retorted.

My mouth went dry and I looked over at Leslie to see her reaction. She looked stunned.

"If she were auditioning for the part, I wasn't informed of that," she insisted. I could see by Leslie's reaction that she did not know.

"Were either of you aware that Miss Gold had been receiving death threats?" he asked as he paused to scratch his chin.

"I haven't talked to Katherine, written Katherine, or seen Katherine until this weekend, so the answer is no, I wasn't aware she was receiving death threats," I decreed. I hoped that was clear enough for "Deputy Dog."

"And you Miss Lane?" he continued.

"I haven't seen Katherine since the Daytime Emmys last year," Leslie admitted.

"But you are in Los Angeles quite a bit for work?" he emphasized.

"I do some work in L.A., but I am currently living in New York doing a show," Leslie replied. She was starting to look very tired. I was concerned about Leslie.

"When you saw Miss Gold at the Emmy's last year, did you speak to her?" Detective Lincoln asked.

"I try to avoid her as much as possible," Leslie chuckled. "We may travel in some of the same circles, but we have *very little* in common," she stressed.

"How about Trenton Sparks?" he blurted and began writing again in his legal pad. "Did you two have Trenton Sparks in common?" he inferred.

For those who have been living under a rock for the last decade, Trenton Sparks is an up and coming Hollywood heart throb who was nominated last year for an Academy Award for his portrayal of a wounded WWII soldier in *American Glory Fighters*. He began his career as a classically trained singer on Broadway and had gradually been transitioning to the big screen. Trenton was a man's man and had wooed many a leading lady over the years.

"Trenton and I were together for a time," Leslie said as she began fidgeting in her chair.

"What happened?" Lincoln inquired innocently.

"We drifted apart. He was in L.A. and I was in New York. It was a bicoastal relationship that ran its course," she retorted.

"So, Katherine Gold had nothing to do with your breakup?" His prominent eyebrows shot up as he waited for her answer.

"No. We had called it quits before he began dating her," she claimed. She crossed her arms and looked defiantly at Detective Lincoln.

"And when would you say your relationship ended?" he questioned.

"Do you want an exact date and time?" she shot at him sarcastically.

"Approximate will be fine," he shrugged and uncrossed his legs. He pushed away from the table and placed his hands behind his head and stretched a bit.

"Around March, I would say," Leslie guessed.

"Around March. So, explain to me this . . . " he said and slid a copy of *People Magazine* across the table. It was dated late January. Spread across the double page story was a beaming Katherine with Trenton Sparks on her arm, pausing for pictures in front of a chic L.A. hotspot. The title was "Trenton Goes for Gold."

"They were introduced at a party my agent, Rick Jones, was throwing. He asked Katherine to show Trenton around L.A.," Leslie explained.

"Show her around L.A.?" he said laughing. "Is that what they call it these days?" Detective Lincoln was obviously enjoying this line of questioning. "When were you aware of their affair?" he persisted.

Leslie's face contorted slightly and her lip began trembling. "I knew something was wrong right away after he left for L.A. I just didn't know what was wrong. I guess I thought he was adjusting and to his new lifestyle. I didn't know it was someone else until much later," she wept.

Leslie had never told me about Trenton. When one is so caught up in family and work, it's easy to let time go by and not get caught up with old friends. I suddenly felt terrible that I had not been there for Leslie during her break up with Trenton. I was the one person who could have understood the betrayal I'm sure she felt. She had been there for me.

Looking back to last spring, I remember talking with Leslie on the phone and she had sounded sad. When I asked what was wrong, she assured me everything was all right and quickly changed the subject. She always was so strong and so independent. I assumed she was okay. I should have paid closer attention! Instead, she began telling me about her next show and how she was starting rehearsals soon.

I am sure that just like with Jett, Trenton was just another conquest for Katherine. That relationship had been over for a while. Pictures of Conrad Ryan, the much younger "boy toy" had been plastered all over the gossip magazines and television gossip shows for a few months. Was he just another publicity stunt or was he a real relationship? Who would ever really know?

"Did you confront Katherine about the affair?" Detective Lincoln demanded.

"No. I was in New York. I just read about it like everyone else. Trenton and I parted ways — *civilly*," Leslie added.

Just then, another detective opened the interview room door.

"Their attorney just arrived. Chief wants to speak to you, Lincoln," he said.

"Ladies, it's been a pleasure. Please don't leave town and I will need to get your contact information before you leave the station," he requested. He smiled and rose from the table and slid his chair under the table.

Cassandra walked in accompanied by a somber looking gentleman who looked to be in his mid-fifties. His curly gray hair, tortoise shell glasses, and serious charcoal grey three piece suit screamed Harvard Law.

"Amelia, Leslie, this is Thomas Simpson, our lead attorney at Reynolds's," Cassandra stated and made introductions.

We shook hands and he gestured for us to remain seated.

"Ladies, the D.A. is still waiting for the coroner's report. At this time, there is no physical reason to believe there has been foul play, but because of the serious nature of the death threats the deceased was receiving, they are treating this as a potential homicide," he recited. He paused, removed his glasses, and cleaned them on his pocket handkerchief. He took his time before he placed them back on the bridge of his nose and continued.

"I need to know where both of you were at the time of Katherine's death and I want you to tell me EVERYTHING that went on at the cocktail party Friday evening. The D.A. has a witness that reported an argument between Miss Gold and Amelia, not to mention an altercation in the skybox between Miss Lane and Miss Gold right before her death," he instructed.

He looked at me with concern on his face. I began feeling the hair stand up on the back of my neck. We were now suspects on a very short list. We had a history, we had a motive, and we had been seen with Katherine right before she died. Someone was setting us up!

Chapter Eleven

We were back in our suite at the Adolphus Hotel. Mr. Simpson decided that the best course of action was to wait to hear a definitive cause of death from the coroner. If Katherine had died from natural causes, there would be no need to worry about a suspect list.

In the meantime, we were reconstructing a timeline for him of what had transpired at the cocktail party and at the Homecoming game.

"I want details, who you were with, what was said, when you saw Katherine, everything," Mr. Simpson requested.

"That shouldn't be too difficult," Olivia joked. "The 'praying mantis' walked in, the paparazzi went wild, she was nasty, what's new?"

"Olivia, this is no time for your wisecracks!" Cassandra admonished. "Please ignore her, Thomas. This is her attempt at humor."

"Need I remind you, Miss Rivers, that you were overheard by one of the catering staff members saying something along the lines of throwing her out by her hair? That remark could end up putting you on the suspect short list," Mr. Simpson stressed and cleared his throat for emphasis.

"I never the met the woman before in my life!" Olivia said defensively. "I was simply reacting to what she had said to Amelia."

"Yes, crimes of passion are usually not premeditated. The perpetrator is reacting to a set of circumstances or events. You would be surprised how many murders were committed under those conditions," Mr. Simpson pointed out.

"Yeah, like remember the woman who ran over her husband with her Mercedes Benz when she found out he was cheating?" Sarah said shaking her head. "Her defense was that she became mentally unstable, temporarily, when she found out he had a mistress."

"I find that hard to believe," Olivia remarked. "She ran over him three times!"

"Ladies, let's focus on the cocktail party," Cassandra reminded everyone.

There was a quick knock on the door. Olivia opened it and Shane entered our suite. I quickly got up from the sofa and rushed to him, throwing my arms around him for a much needed embrace. We stood there, holding each other, oblivious to everyone else in the room.

"Shane, let me introduce you to Thomas Simpson," Cassandra said as Shane ended our embrace and they shook hands. "He's been our head legal advisor at Reynolds's for the last fifteen years. I trust him explicitly to handle the most delicate legal aspects of our personal and business dealings," she reassured Shane.

"Thank you so much, Mr. Simpson. I was relieved to hear that Amelia had top-notch legal counsel when I heard what had transpired over the last two days," Shane sighed.

"Shane, would you like something to drink?" Sarah asked, motioning him to come in and sit down. "Maybe some coffee, iced tea?"

"More like a gin and tonic, I'm betting," Olivia suggested.

"Actually, a strong drink would be good about now. Anyone care to join me?" Shane offered.

While the men got down to business and discussed strategy, Leslie and I stepped outside on the terrace for some fresh air.

"I can't believe this is all happening, Amelia," she cried as she looked out at the Dallas skyline. "One minute we're exchanging our usual barbed remarks, and the next minute Katherine is dead!" She began crying and shaking her head, covering her face with her hands.

"I know, I know," I empathized and wrapped my arms around her. "This has been so surreal. Can you think of anyone who would have wanted to kill her?

"Well, I know she had a reputation for being difficult, but I can't imagine that being a reason," Leslie speculated.

"What about this thing with Trenton? Why didn't you tell me, Leslie?" I finally asked.

Leslie admitted, "I was humiliated, embarrassed and it was the same song and dance, just different boyfriend. I knew better than to allow my agent to introduce the two of them. It was my own dumb fault!" She was getting angry and clenching her hands at her sides into fists.

"And then to top it off, to find out from the detective that Katherine was being considered for the SAME role in the Ron Howard movie. I had no idea. I was told I had first right of refusal," she snapped.

"Maybe Detective Lincoln was setting you up to get a reaction out of you," I pointed out to her.

"Yes, maybe he was and that is exactly why I don't want either of you talking to him again without me being present. I would have never allowed you to answer his questions. The coroner hasn't even ruled this as homicide," Mr. Simpson chided as he joined us out on the terrace.

"Shane was just filling me in on your past relationship with Miss Gold. Amelia, you have motive. It's as simple as that," he concluded.

"I may have been upset with Katherine, but I would never hurt her!" I retorted.

"That may be true, but the police don't see it that way. Infidelity is the number one cause of murder by women in the U.S." Simpson explained and took another sip of his drink.

"But that was twenty years ago! I am happily married and have moved on!" I objected. *What was going on here? Was I really going to have to dredge all this up again?* I thought to myself.

"Leslie has motive as well. She also ended a relationship because of Miss Gold and there was the potential of losing a big movie part. People have killed for a lot less," he reminded us.

"Do you think I did it? If you do, I don't want you representing me!" Leslie declared as she looked sternly at Mr. Simpson.

"Defense attorneys don't care if their client is guilty or innocent. It's irrelevant to me," he admitted and held his hands palms up.

"But it's relevant to me!" Leslie was becoming angry. "You will try a heck of a lot harder to defend me if you believe in my innocence in the first place."

She was right about that. I know defense attorneys will create a solid defense whether or not their client is innocent or guilty, but knowing without a doubt that their client was innocent would make it easier to represent someone, it would seem to me.

"Mr. Simpson," I acknowledged, "I know you are just doing your job. But, Leslie was with me in the skybox when Katherine died. She couldn't have killed her."

"Do you have witnesses that can verify that fact?" Simpson challenged.

"Yes, of course! Olivia, Sarah, and Cassandra were there with us as well as all the other VIP's SMU hosted that day.

"I want you to think of everyone that was there. Who were you introduced to, who did you speak with, everyone. This is vitally important to your case," Mr. Simpson implored.

Case? I hope it didn't even get that far.

Shane came out on the terrace, a worried expression across his handsome face.

"When will you hear something from the coroner's office?" he asked Simpson.

"Tomorrow morning at the earliest," Mr. Simpson answered. "We should have a preliminary cause of death as well as a rudimentary toxicology screening. If we are lucky, the coroner will find out she had heart disease, an enlarged heart or something along those lines."

"I think the coroner will find she didn't have a heart at all," Olivia smirked and stood by the open French doors.

"Stop that Olivia," Sarah said and swatted her on the arm. She began laughing.

We all got a little tickled at that point. It was almost a relief to find a little humor in the midst of such a tragic situation.

"Well, I will leave my cell phone number and please feel free to call me at any time if you think of anything that will help your case," Mr. Simpson requested and turned to leave.

"Thank you, Thomas!" Cassandra said and kissed him on the cheek.

"Mr. Simpson, thank you again," Shane said and shook his hand profusely. "I think we will all sleep better knowing we have such esteemed representation."

Did he really think I would be able to sleep? Sleep was the last thing on my mind. I needed to think. Think about who would want to hurt Katherine. Think about how I was innocent! Think about my kids and my family. Kids! I had not even thought to ask Shane who was watching Emma and Charlie!

"Yes, thank you Mr. Simpson," I said shaking the fog from my brain.

Cassandra ushered him from the suite and the rest of us sat down, emotionally worn out from the day's activities.

"Shane, how are Emma and Charlie? Who's watching them while you are here?" I wondered.

"Sweetheart, Aunt Alice agreed to stay as long as she is needed. She thought it would be a wonderful opportunity to spoil both of them with some special one-on-one time," Shane said.

"Thank goodness for Aunt Alice!" I reaffirmed and sighed deeply. She had really been such a lifesaver this week with helping out with The Pink Dogwood Tea Room and now the kids. We were lucky to have such a good support team in our family.

"Speaking of Aunt Alice and the kids, I'm going to give them a call and let them know all is well and I arrived safely!" he added and turned to step out onto the terrace to use his cell phone.

"Shane, tell them I will call and tuck them in for the night in a little bit. Give Aunt Alice my love!" I requested. He nodded and closed the French doors behind him.

"I've got to make a list of people who had an ax to grind with Katherine," I stated and walked over to the hotel desk to grab stationary and a pen.

"Why don't I order room service while you guys work on that," Cassandra volunteered.

"Put me down for a T-bone, garlic mashed potatoes, a side salad with the house dressing, and a large slice of chocolate silk pie," Olivia ordered. "Oh, and can you ask for some dinner rolls with that?" she concluded.

"Anything else you want 'Jabba the Hut?'" Cassandra teased her.

"I'll take fajitas and whatever else," Sarah added trying to be easy.

"Amelia, how about you?" Cassandra asked.

"I don't think I have much of an appetite right now, but thanks Cassandra. I think I need ibuprofen and a good night's sleep. Maybe some herbal tea and a few crackers," I answered. I was very worried about what Mr. Simpson had discussed with us.

"Leslie, how about you?" Cassandra inquired.

"Unlike Amelia, I eat when I am stressed. Order for me whatever you're getting. I am not particular in the slightest," she smiled and sat down next to me.

"Okay. I'll check with Shane and then call room service and place our orders," Cassandra reported. She seemed glad just to stay busy tonight. We were all a bit jumpy and nervous after a long day at the police headquarters and strategizing with Mr. Simpson.

"All right, Leslie. Let's think about who was at the cocktail party, who spoke with Katherine, who had a past with Katherine and who had access to her at homecoming," I asserted. I was ready to get down to business and put all this behind me.

"Monica," she stated point blank.

"Monica?" I was surprised she would consider her at all. She was always so quiet and sweet.

"Yes. She had motive. She was Katherine's sister, always in her shadow, always cleaning up her messes, never leading her own life," Leslie declared.

"Okay. We'll put Monica down." Leslie was right. Monica was with Katherine in the skybox and most likely went with her to the football field. She had been orchestrating interviews with the paparazzi when we last saw her. No doubt she was on the sidelines doing the same thing right before Katherine died.

"Anyone else?" I asked Leslie.

"Jett," she continued nonchalantly.

"Jett?" I couldn't believe she had even suggested that!

"Jett was at the cocktail party. Remember he came up and told Katherine to back off?" she reminded me.

Yes, he had told Katherine to back off and he had been very apologetic about the way things had turned out. Maybe he was regretting what he did more than I knew. But that was ridiculous! Jett was happy with Laura and the twins. Why would he put his family in jeopardy?

"I don't remember seeing Jett at homecoming," I thought out loud.

"You don't remember seeing him in the skybox, but no doubt he was at the game. He didn't come all the way to Dallas just for a cocktail party, I'm sure!" Olivia interjected.

"Olivia's right, Amelia," Leslie persisted. She had crossed her arms and began nodding her head in agreement. Her green cat eyes were narrowed in deep thought. "Anyone at that game could have had access to the field when Katherine was getting her award," she pointed out.

"The Jett I knew was never capable of hurting someone," I said defensively.

"Honey, the Jett you knew wouldn't have cheated with Katherine, but he did," Cassandra said placing a hand on my shoulder. "Let's face it, Amelia. How well did you actually know Jett?" she challenged.

That was a good question. At one time, I would have told you I knew him almost as well as I knew myself. The day I found him in bed with Katherine, I realized I didn't know him at all. Maybe he was capable of something as vicious as murder, but we were getting ahead of ourselves.

"We haven't even heard back from the coroner yet, so why are we assuming she was murdered?" I cautioned the group.

"Well, for starters, the police are suspecting foul play for some reason," Sarah interjected. "They don't usually do that unless there is some evidence. Maybe the hospital uncovered something." She sat down next to me and started twisting her hair, her old habit when she is deep in thought.

Sarah was right. Detective Lincoln wouldn't jeopardize his case by jumping the gun before the coroner's report unless there was some evidence that led the police to believe she had been murdered. This was not just a "high profile" death that they were taking extra precautions about; they had evidence suggesting Katherine's death was not by natural causes. I would have to go down to the police station in the morning and ask Detective Lincoln what was going on. In the meantime, we would work on the suspect list.

"Emma, Charlie, and Aunt Alice send their love, sweetheart!" Shane told me giving me a brief update of their activities. "Aunt Alice said not to worry about the tea room. She has everything under control and she's been having a ball." He came in and took a seat around the coffee table. "How are you coming along with the list?" he asked glancing at it sideways. "Monica and Jett?"

"Monica is Katherine's younger sister who is basically her slave-in-waiting," Olivia gladly informed him. "Her joy in life is cleaning up after her sister's illicit love affairs and dealing with the paparazzi." She sat down on the arm of the sofa and arched her trademark eyebrows. "That's a full time job and one I wouldn't relish," she quipped.

"Why Jett?" Shane asked and looked over at me for an answer.

"Jett confronted Katherine at the cocktail party two nights ago when she started giving Amelia a hard time," Olivia enjoyed telling him. "Don't worry, Shane, I took care of her," she gloated.

"And could end up as a possible suspect in all of this if Katherine's death is ruled a murder," Cassandra added, glaring at Olivia.

"Sounds like I missed quite a cocktail party!" Shane joked to the group of ladies surrounding him. "What exactly happened?"

We all took turns giving our best imitation of Katherine's entrance to the party, her vampy posing for the paparazzi and her rude remarks.

"And then I told Amelia, I would have thrown her out by her 'Goldilocks' if I had caught her in bed with my fiancée and according to the police, one of the catering crew overheard my remark," Olivia sheepishly admitted.

"Who didn't hear you, Olivia?" Cassandra chastised her. "You know how loud you get after you've been nipping the tequila," she reminded her.

Olivia turned a few shades of red and got defensive. "Look, it was only two shots of very fine tequila, I might add. It was nothing like my night of riding the electric bull. I was under control," she snapped. She got up and began adjusting her jeans. "When's dinner getting here?" she asked obviously wanting to change the subject.

"That's Olivia," Cassandra decreed, "a slave to her appetite!"

"You guys are so funny!" Leslie said laughing out loud. "I love the dynamics of your friendships."

"Yeah, it's like *Steel Magnolias* on steroids. Cassandra is Shirley MacLaine's character, Wheezer!" Olivia jested as she cracked up at her own joke.

"You take that back right now!" Cassandra demanded and chased Olivia around the room. "Take that back this instant! I'll show you Wheezer!" She began throwing pillows at Olivia. It was good to let out all the pent up stress from the day's events.

"Ladies, ladies, we better keep it down before the hotel calls the police and then we REALLY will be in trouble!" Shane yelled out. He shook his head, laughing at the scene in front of him.

Little did Shane know the trouble that tomorrow would bring to the "Traveling Tea Ladies." Today was just a warm up for what lay ahead.

Chapter Twelve

I managed to get a few hours of uninterrupted sleep before I woke up with my mental list of suspects. I decided to sneak out of bed and let Shane sleep in while I ordered some hot tea. Luckily, the Adolphus hotel had a nice selection of loose teas to choose from. After deciding on some chocolate croissants, fresh fruit salad, herb and goat cheese omelets, a nice pot of English breakfast tea, and a strong pot of Kenyan coffee, I quickly showered before room service arrived. I dressed and got ready for the day.

I heard a quiet knock at the door, and ushered the room service attendant inside. With quiet efficiency, he set the dining room table for six and dropped off the morning newspaper. I tipped him and thanked him as I closed the door.

"Good Morning, Amelia!" Leslie said as she wiped the sleep from her eyes. "How did you sleep?" She stretched and yawned, her arms extended above her head.

"I slept some. I thought maybe after a nice breakfast, we might take a trip over to campus and do a little investigating of our own," I suggested.

"Did I hear someone say breakfast?" Olivia excitedly said as she rushed into the room.

"Morning, Liv! How did you sleep?" I asked her.

She continued belting her green silk robe and took a seat. "I slept okay. I sleep better at home with the sounds of the river outside my window," she admitted and began eyeballing the chocolate croissants. I knew I better get everyone else up before she ate more than her fair share.

"Hold it right there, Olivia Rivers!" Cassandra warned pointing at her. "Step away from the croissant and you won't get hurt!" She had already dressed in a snappy black sweater set with hounds tooth checked pants. She was such a classic, right down to her large pearl earrings.

"Good morning, everyone!" Sarah said as she came into the room wearing a kimono style silk robe in bright turquoise. It had a brilliant ceremonial dragon embroidered across the back.

I went around the table and poured everyone their choice of coffee or English breakfast tea. Some habits just die hard. I am used to waiting on everyone. It was good to stay busy this morning. It helped to steady my nerves.

The chocolate croissants were decadent and I enjoyed every bite! They were almost as good as "La Madeleine's," a French patisserie near campus that I loved to patron. We all were rather quiet as we ate our omelets. Finally, after a second cup of coffee, we were all revived and ready to strategize.

"If we have to be stuck in Dallas for a day or two, you guys might as well do some shopping and sightseeing and make the best of it," I suggested to the table which now included Shane who still had damp hair from his shower.

"Look, Amelia and Leslie. We are here to support you guys. We can shop and sightsee another time," Cassandra pointed out and looked around the table for confirmation.

"I agree with Cassandra," Sarah said quietly. "I wouldn't feel right about shopping knowing that you are going through all this!"

"How can we help, Amelia?" Olivia asked taking another bite of her second croissant. "Anyone have any ideas?" she inquired. She licked her fingers and continued eating.

"I've been thinking that we should return to the scene of the crime and talk to anyone who might have seen anything during the half-time show," I told them.

"Good idea, Amelia," Shane agreed with me. "But first, I am going to go by the police station and talk with Detective Lincoln and see if he's heard from the coroner's department yet. Ladies, if you'll excuse me," he said politely.

"There's no need, Shane," Cassandra informed him showing him the front page of *The Dallas Morning News*. "The preliminary autopsy report is in," she pronounced.

The headline screamed, "Golden Girl Dies By Apparent Poisoning." A grotesque picture of Katherine being wheeled away on the paramedic's gurney was under the caption. An oxygen mask was on her face, her eyes were closed, her skin was slightly blue, and her platinum blonde hair was disheveled.

"Poisoned?" Olivia asked incredulously. "I can't believe it!" she said loudly.

Shane read on: "The initial toxicology reports have shown a lethal level of an unknown poison in her blood stream. It will be a few more days before they identify the poison. Police are looking for the source and delivery method." He was shaking his head in disbelief. We were all rather somber as this information sank in.

"Who would do that to her?" Leslie demanded, anger barely contained in her voice. "What a terrible way to die!"

"Maybe it was something she ate," I offered to the group. "Did anyone see her eat while she was in the skybox?" I began replaying Katherine's entrance into the VIP room over in my mind.

"I don't remember her eating anything!" Olivia piped in.

"You would know," Cassandra said seriously, "Since you planted yourself right next to the buffet most of the first half."

"She's right," Sarah affirmed confidently. "Olivia, did Katherine even get that close to where you were standing?"

129

"No, after I made that Botox remark, I moved back over by the oysters in the half shell. Katherine never came close to me after that," Olivia confirmed.

"What Botox remark? Never mind! I don't want to know!" Shane said looking at Olivia. "You were never one to mince words."

"Maybe she was poisoned in her drink," Sarah speculated. "Did anyone see her being served a drink?" she asked excitedly.

"No. I don't remember her holding a drink," Leslie murmured. "As I recall, she was being interviewed most of the time she was in the skybox. She was also busy being introduced to all those Texas big wigs, politicians and oil men," she remembered.

"Maybe someone handed her a bottle of water on the way to the field. Maybe the water was spiked with the poison," I suggested.

We all began nodding our heads, deep in thought, trying to figure out how she could have been poisoned.

"Who would know if she had something to drink after she left the skybox?" Shane asked.

"The one person I can think of is her sister, Monica Gold," I told Shane.

"Girls, we've got to find out where she's staying and talk with her. Maybe she saw something that could clear our names," I announced.

"Hurry up, Olivia and get dressed!" Cassandra snapped at her. "We've got to find Monica and fast before she leaves town."

"I'll be just a minute!" Olivia said and dashed from the table.

"Wait for me, too!" Sarah called back looking over her shoulder.

"I will try to make a few phone calls to L.A. and see if anyone out there knew what hotel Katherine and Monica were booked in. I'll be right back," Cassandra added and grabbed her cell phone out of her black patent leather clutch and headed to the terrace for privacy.

"I hope Cassandra can find Monica before she flies out," I said beginning to get very anxious. What if she did leave town? How would we be able to find out what or who she had seen with Katherine? We just had to clear our names and the only way to do that was to figure out who killed Katherine and how.

"I hope we're not too late!" Leslie said running her fingers through her long black hair. She had started to get dark circles under her eyes. She definitely had not slept much the past two days.

"I don't think Monica will leave until the coroner releases Katherine's body. I think you will have some time to track her down," Shane hoped. He was still reading the paper, studying it for clues of what might have happened.

"Did you know that they just announced that a special tribute is being planned for Katherine at next month's Emmys?" Shane asked us. "She will be receiving a lifetime achievement award, posthumous, of course," he informed us.

"I'm going to flip on the television while we are waiting for Olivia and Sarah to get ready. I want to see the local weather forecast. I never know if October will be warm or cool in Dallas," I recalled and rose from the table. The local news was plastering pictures of Katherine from the cocktail party and her collapse on the field. They even had footage of her gurney being rolled into the coroner's office. I quickly turned off the television. It was just too much for me to take in.

"She's bigger now than she was when she was alive," Leslie remarked to Shane and me.

"Yes, she is," said Cassandra coming through the terrace doors. "My Hollywood contacts just told me that Andrew Morton is writing a tell-all book about her life. It is a million dollar book deal," Cassandra announced to all.

"Isn't he the same author who wrote about Princess Diana?" Shane asked surprised by this news.

"Yes and Posh and Beck and Madonna and Tom Cruise and currently Angelina Jolie," Olivia blurted out as she came into the room wearing a smart looking brown bolero jacket, dark denim dress jeans, and ankle high dark chocolate brown boots.

"When did you become the official celebrity gossip queen?" Cassandra said in a belittling tone. She crossed her arms waiting to hear her response.

"Well, I guess in order to keep up with you and all your 'Holly-Weird' friends I have been doing a little celebrity reading," Olivia retorted.

"Yeah like what!" Cassandra argued and threw her head back in astonishment.

"I don't know—*People Magazine*, maybe *US Weekly*," she admitted.

"YOU! YOU are reading *People* and *US Weekly!* I don't believe it. Since when?" Cassandra challenged.

"I'm ready!" Sarah announced coming into the room wearing black leggings, a long black tunic and a matching black beret.

"What are you, some character from *The Pink Panther* dressed for undercover surveillance?" Olivia teased her. At least she and Cassandra had temporarily stopped talking about Olivia's celebrity gossip sources.

"I figured I should dress the part. You never know when you'll need to blend in," Sarah told Olivia with a pert nod of her head.

"I don't exactly call that blending in since berets are usually a French fashion trend, but okay," Olivia conceded.

Sarah put a very large dark pair of sunglasses on. She definitely looked as though she was working for the CIA or some French undercover agency. She tickled me with her costumes. I went over and wrapped my arm around her neck and laughed.

"No one can say that we are dull, that's for sure!" I laughed. We definitely were an interesting group.

"OK! Carl's waiting with the car and I have Monica's hotel information." Cassandra announced and led the way to the hotel elevators. "What's the plan for you, Shane?" she asked.

"I am meeting with Thomas Simpson at the station to talk with Detective Lincoln. I want more details about Katherine's autopsy and to see what leads Lincoln has at this point," Shane answered. He was wearing a light weight navy blue cable knit sweater over a baby blue button down shirt paired with khaki pants and fringed loafers. He was calm and collected but with a determined look in his eyes!

"Do you really think Detective Lincoln will share privileged information with you?" I asked him as I straightened his collar and smoothed his sweater.

"I don't know, but I can't sit around here going stir crazy. I've got to try," he said as he gave me a kiss before getting on the elevator. "I will call you and tell you what I find out. You ladies need to be careful today. You don't want to go poking your noses where they don't belong," he warned us.

Chapter Thirteen

Carl drove us to the Crescent Hotel, a European style beauty in the center of Dallas. It was every bit as lavish as the Adolphus, but it had a much different feel. It was among the most upscale hotels in country.

We stepped into the lavishly appointed lobby and waited in the lounge for Monica to join us. Cassandra had phoned ahead to let her know we were on our way. She had seemed very receptive to our impromptu visit.

"Monica, I am so sorry for your loss!" I lamented and squeezed her tight.

"Thank you, Amelia. Thank you," she mumbled almost in a daze. Her face was drawn and void of color. She was wearing a simple navy blue pair of slacks with a white button down blouse. She wiped her nose on a tissue and gestured for us to join her at a table near the window.

"Monica, I would like you to meet my friends from Dogwood Cove. Olivia Rivers, Cassandra Reynolds and Sarah Smith," I began.

"Hello, so nice to meet all of you," she said shaking hands with everyone.

"Monica, I'm so sorry!" Leslie said and gave her a heartfelt hug. Monica began crying and took off her glasses and dabbed her eyes with a worn tissue.

"I just can't believe Katherine is gone! She was all the family I had and I just feel so lost," Monica cried.

I reached out and squeezed Monica's arm and offered her reassurance. Sarah, Olivia, and Cassandra had begun to tear up as well.

"Amelia, Leslie. I can't tell you how much I appreciate your support right now. Katherine really didn't have many friends and it would mean so much to her to know that you were helping me right now," she acknowledged.

"Do you have any idea what happened to her?" I asked, hoping to get down to the facts.

"No. She was fine. We did interviews and she posed for the paparazzi the entire walk down to the field. She was fine!" she insisted. Monica had begun bawling as she recounted the events of Katherine's last moments.

"Monica, honey," Leslie said in a very soothing tone. "The paper this morning is saying she was poisoned. Do you have any idea when she could have been exposed to poison or how?" Leslie asked.

"She seemed fine. We ate breakfast together and she didn't complain of feeling sick or tired. In fact, we both ordered the same thing. She was very excited to receive her award," Monica added.

"Could someone have handed her bottled water or something to drink that could have been laced with a toxin?" I asked her. "Maybe it happened on the way to the field at half-time?" I suggested.

"She was offered something to drink, but refused because she didn't want to mess up her makeup. I remember her turning down something to drink. She knew it was a big photo op for her and was very particular about her appearance," Monica recalled.

So, it was not her breakfast, if Monica was not the one who poisoned her and they both ate the same thing. She had not had anything to eat or drink in the skybox or on the way to the field.

How then could someone have administered poison to Katherine? I was perplexed. Nothing was adding up.

"Monica, dear, I don't mean to upset you with what I'm about to suggest, but it has to be mentioned. Was Katherine having problems with anyone at work?" Cassandra asked her, squeezing her hand.

Monica began rolling her tissue over and over in her hands. She seemed very uncomfortable with Cassandra's question.

She began speaking, her voice quivery, "Katherine was not the easiest person to get along with. She didn't make many friends on set, especially since she worked with so many women," Monica admitted.

She was visibly shaken and Sarah went to go get her a glass of water from the wait staff.

"Here you go, sweetie!" Sarah said and patted her shoulders. "Drink this and try to calm down," she offered. Sarah had a calming effect on most people she met. Monica looked up appreciatively at Sarah and continued.

"Katherine was a very vital woman . . . she had many lovers," she revealed and cleared her throat, stopping to sip some more water. "Some of the men she was involved with were married, some were co-worker's boyfriends, she just couldn't understand what off-limits meant," Monica sighed as she cast a sideways look over at me and sank down a bit in her chair. She must have known about Jett and Katherine.

"Is there anyone you can think of that was angry enough to want to hurt her?" Leslie asked Monica. "This is really important. Maybe a jealous co-worker, an ex lover, a fan?"

"She was receiving some fan mail that began as just someone criticizing Katherine's personal life, but it became increasingly scary over time. They were sending pictures of Katherine cut up and re-pasted with images of blood and skulls in the background. It was very disturbing," she shivered as she recalled the gruesome mail.

"How many of these did she receive?" I asked her.

"Maybe ten at the most over the past three months. The F.B.I. has all of them and has been analyzing them," Monica claimed.

"Could this demented person been at the homecoming game? I mean, did you notice anyone behaving strangely or following you around?" I asked her, hoping she would remember a face and description.

"There was a man with the paparazzi who made some very inappropriate remarks to Katherine," she remembered. "He wasn't someone I recognized from L.A. He was at the cocktail party and at the homecoming game taking pictures. I did my best to keep Katherine as far away from him as possible," she assured us.

"What did he look like?" Leslie asked hopefully.

"He had dark brown hair," she paused, deep in thought, "what sounded like maybe an Italian accent, and he was wearing a baseball cap. He kept screaming at her, calling her a slut and home wrecker," Monica said.

Olivia averted her eyes and then looked across the table at me. I think she was thinking what we all were thinking. Katherine had wrecked a lot of relationships and had a reputation of being promiscuous. The photographer's comment was mild in comparison of some of the things our sorority sisters had said to her in years past when she stole their boyfriends.

"You mentioned you were not familiar with him. Do you have any idea what magazine or paper he was representing?" Sarah asked Monica.

"No, I have no idea. I told the police about him though and they are reviewing footage from the cocktail party gala to see if they can identify him in the crowd of paparazzi. Maybe they will get lucky," Monica hoped.

"Monica, dear," Cassandra began hesitantly, "was there anyone on set who had it out for Katherine, someone who may have made threats to her?"

"Well, yes. Like I said, Katherine had a lot of male attention. Sometimes that caused friction on set when she got involved with her co-workers significant others or her male co-stars," she remarked.

"We're not here to judge," Sarah said sitting down next to Monica. "We just want to help find who did this and bring justice to Katherine. Anything you can think of will help us to help the police," Sarah offered.

Thank goodness Sarah had come with us. She was a stabilizing factor at the moment. I was also glad Olivia was remaining quiet.

"She had recently had an affair with Bo Bronson and it had not ended well," Monica claimed. *Bo Bronson. Bo Bronson?* I wracked my brain, but I couldn't remember who he was.

"Bo Bronson plays Thad on 'The Rich and The Lost,'" Olivia informed me when she saw the puzzled look on my face. "He is one of the established characters on the show," she shrugged.

Cassandra tried to hide her amusement with Olivia. "Gee, Olivia, I had no idea you knew so much about the soaps!" Cassandra teased.

"So," I said ignoring the exchange. "What happened with Bo?"

"Well, he fell madly in love with Katherine. It was hot and steady for a few months. His wife, Sheila, found out and was furious! She showed up on the set and caused quite a scene, on one occasion interrupting filming for an entire day. They are now in the middle of a very nasty custody battle and divorce," Monica conceded.

"And then what happened?" I asked.

"Bo proposed, but she had started seeing Conrad by then, and Bo got crazed with jealousy," Monica claimed. "He threatened Conrad and said he would make Katherine pay for ruining his marriage, for two timing him, and making him look like a fool."

Monica was twisting her tissue again and becoming very agitated. Recalling all the recent events was no doubt hard on her.

"How about a hot pot of chamomile tea to settle our nerves," I suggested.

"I think that sounds like a good idea. I'll go find someone and order it," Sarah volunteered.

"She had decided to leave the show because of Bo," Monica admitted. "She just couldn't deal with his jealousy every day at work."

Cassandra shot me a quizzical look and we all turned our attention back to Monica.

"The talk around Hollywood is that Katherine's contract wasn't being renewed. Is there any truth to it?" Cassandra asked her with sincere concern in her voice.

"Yes and no," Monica paused and slipped her glasses off again. Her eyes were red and swollen as if she had been crying for days. "Sheila Bronson's uncle is one of the producers of 'The Rich and The Lost.' Sheila wanted heads to roll after she found out about Bo's affair. She wanted Katherine gone. Katherine was more than happy to leave. She was really scared of Bo. She said he was following her. He refused to accept it was over and wanted her back at any cost. And his wife, Sheila, had some very powerful friends. She vowed to ruin Katherine's career," Monica recounted.

Wow. It sounded like the last few months had been horrible for Katherine. She had a scorned wife to deal with and a jealous ex-lover! No wonder she was making plans to return to Dallas. It sounded like she was running away from a nightmare.

"What do you mean Bo was following her?" I asked.

Monica answered, "He would park his car outside of Katherine's home at all hours of the night. There was one time, he showed up at the restaurant where Conrad and Katherine were dining. He had hacked into her cell phone calendar and found out her dinner plans. He made a big scene and punched Conrad. They had to forget dinner and leave the restaurant," she recounted.

"Oh, I remember hearing about that! Didn't Bo get arrested for assault?" Olivia recalled.

"Yes, yes he did and there was a restraining order issued. She was very scared of him. It was like he turned into a monster! If he couldn't have her, he didn't want anyone else to have her," Monica claimed.

"Did you tell all this to the police?" Cassandra asked her.

"No. I didn't really think it had anything to do with Katherine's collapse. I just assumed she died from a heart attack," Monica admitted. Her shoulders began shaking again and she laid her head on my shoulder. I put my arm around her and held her close. Poor Monica! She was left all alone now.

Sarah returned with our server and hot chamomile tea for all of us. We spent the next few minutes pouring tea and holding our tea cups, feeling the soothing hot liquid coat our throats and warm our hands. We had all become very quiet thinking about everything Monica had shared with us.

"How was your relationship with Katherine?" I calmly asked her. "I know you were acting as her assistant. It must have been difficult to be her sister and work for her too," I persisted. I knew I was prying into her personal relationship with Katherine, but this might be my only chance to talk with Monica. I was willing to push her to get my name cleared and Monica was the last one who was seen with Katherine. She was also very vulnerable at this moment.

"Our relationship had its ups and downs. She was very trying at times," Monica disclosed.

That was an understatement. Monica was being generous. She took another sip of tea and set down her cup on her saucer.

"It wasn't my idea to be her assistant, but she had a hard time finding good help. They would work with her for a few weeks, and then quit. She said I was the only one who understood her," she acknowledged and let out a sob and wiped her nose. "I put my college education on hold to help her. Now what am I going to do?"

"You don't have to figure anything out right now, honey," Cassandra reassured her. "But, when you are ready, go back to school. Education will open all kind of doors for you."

"I'm thinking of a career change right now," Sarah divulged. "I think a change will do you good, too!" She patted her arm and poured Monica another cup of tea.

Monica rambled, "Don't get me wrong. I loved my sister. It just wasn't my idea of living life; answering fan mail, making appointments, booking hotels and travel, dealing with paparazzi. Some days it was just too much!" She pushed her bobbed hair back with both of her hands and exhaled deeply. "Katherine thought I should be grateful that she gave me a job. She just didn't get it that I lost who I was and what I wanted for myself in the process. It was all about her! I know that sounds awful, but I have been going to a therapist for a while to work out some of my feelings," she confessed. Monica looked around the table for support.

I nodded in agreement. Monica had devoted her life to Katherine and from what I could tell, recently life with Katherine had been very unpleasant. Monica would need to take some time for herself and figure out her next step.

"How is Conrad holding up?" Leslie asked her.

"I haven't spoken with him. He and Katherine called it quits a few weeks ago when she decided to move back to Dallas. Neither of them was good at long distance relationships and his career is in L.A. He's with someone else now," Monica mentioned.

"Who is it? Penelope Cruz, Jennifer Aniston, Cameron Diaz maybe?" Olivia asked hanging on the edge of her chair.

"Olivia, get a grip!" Cassandra chided her! "Who cares who Conrad's dating?"

"Was Katherine seeing anyone here in Dallas, maybe?" I suggested.

"I'm not aware of anyone. Though, she was being secretive about some meetings that were not on her appointment book, but if she was seeing someone new, I certainly didn't know," Monica frowned.

"Just to let you know, Monica, Leslie and I have been questioned by the Dallas police and we are on a short list of suspects," I informed her.

"You and Leslie? What are they thinking?" She asked, stunned with her mouth open in surprise.

"He's thinking Amelia is still heartbroken over Jett," Olivia interrupted. "And Leslie is still heartbroken over Trenton," she blurted.

"That's preposterous!" Monica said shaking her head furiously. "You three were so close in college. There is no way you would ever hurt Katherine," she observed.

"Thank you for saying that," I told her and gave her a hug. "All that stuff is ancient history as far as I'm concerned," I added.

Monica and I had shared some good times when she visited Katherine. I think we must have watched *Dirty Dancing* at least twenty times. I recall she had a fierce crush on Patrick Swayze.

"It's definitely ancient history for me as well," Leslie agreed.

The weekends Monica had visited, Leslie and I had usually managed entertaining her while Katherine was out with her latest conquest. We both felt bad for the way Katherine didn't take time for her younger sister and we could tell she felt slighted. She never complained about being overlooked.

"You weren't even near Katherine when she collapsed. Why would they suspect you guys?"

"Detective Lincoln is going on our past history, I am presuming. I think it would really help the police if you could trace exactly what happened on the sidelines before Katherine received her award," I strongly suggested to her.

"Yes. I've, I've, I have been trying to remember everything," Monica stammered.

"Start with who was near Katherine on the sidelines," Olivia began. "Did you notice anyone suspicious, maybe someone out of place or wearing dark sunglasses and a hat?"

"We were all wearing sunglasses, Olivia!" Cassandra said exasperated. "It was a sunny day. No one in Dallas goes anywhere without their sunglasses," she snorted.

"I just thought it might help her to remember," Olivia said defensively and crossed her arms glaring at Cassandra.

"What do you remember happening right before Katherine walked onto the field to receive her award?" Leslie interjected. She fiddled with her teaspoon and finally rested it on the back of her saucer. She seemed to have a lot of nervous energy, as we all did.

Monica concentrated and answered, "We stopped and did a few short interviews on our way to the field. One with the reporter from the Fox affiliate in Dallas, one with NBC who was televising the game and then we stopped at the fifty yard line to wait for Katherine's award."

Monica was staring down at the table, tracing patterns on the white linen tablecloth with her index finger. She took another sip of her tea. Her hand shook slightly as she brought the teacup up to her lips.

We all sat quietly around the table, allowing Monica time to gather her thoughts. She set the teacup back on her saucer and continued.

Monica resumed, "I have wracked my brain trying to think of anyone that might have had contact with her. By the time we reached the field, the players had gone into the locker rooms, the band was playing and we waited with the SMU president to walk out on the field." She shook her head, bewildered by what could have possibly happened. "I just don't get it. How could anyone have poisoned her? I was with her the entire time. I didn't see anyone or anything unusual. This is just not adding up!" she cried.

She banged her fists on the table, her frustration fully visible. Monica set her head down on her crossed arms and began crying again.

Sarah came over and began gently rubbing her back in circles. She held her hand and began soothing her.

"There, there, Monica. Hush, hush. Just breathe deeply," Sarah said as she stroked her back. She had such a maternal way about her.

Monica slowly lifted her head, dabbed her nose and thanked Sarah. Obviously, this had been a very difficult conversation for her to have with us.

Hopefully, we would learn something to help the police track down the killer.

"So then, Katherine walked out with President Turner," Leslie thought out loud. That's when he got on the microphone and made the presentation to the crowd," she paused.

"And then he placed the tiara on her head," Olivia interrupted and lifted an imaginary tiara in the air and placing it on. "She then walked across the field and waved to the crowd," Olivia finished and pantomimed her Miss America wave, "and then she collapsed."

"How could the poison have been administered?" Monica wondered between sobs. "I was there the whole time! We ate together. I stood right next to her during her interviews. I don't see how this could have happened," she sobbed.

"Don't worry, Monica. We'll get to the bottom of this. I think we need to pay a visit to Ford stadium and see what we can find out," I suggested and looked around the table for confirmation from the girls.

"Amelia, why don't I stay here with Monica and keep her company. She's got a lot going on," Sarah suggested.

"You don't have to, Sarah. I'm really all right," Monica insisted as she blew her nose and adjusted her glasses.

"Sweetheart, you've been through quite an ordeal," Cassandra reminded her in her kindest Southern drawl. "Sarah is right. Someone should stay with you. You shouldn't be alone right now," she said.

"It's decided, then!" Sarah said with determination and patted Monica's hand. "Let's get you back to your room, and I will prepare a nice hot bubble bath for you!"

"Sarah, you've got your cell phone on you, right?" I reminded her. "We'll head over to the campus and catch up with you later," I told her.

"Come on Monica," Sarah ordered and assisted her from the table. We watched as the two approached the bank of elevators and the doors closed behind them.

"What do you think of all of this, Amelia?" Cassandra questioned. "She just came up with a whole list of suspects: Bo Bronson, Sheila Bronson, the Italian photographer, whoever sent the threatening letters," she recited.

"And don't forget the police suspect you, me and Jett," Leslie added with a sarcastic laugh.

"And then there are the mysterious appointments Katherine kept secret from her sister. Maybe she had another lover?" Cassandra insinuated.

"You're forgetting the one person who had the most access to Katherine and motive as well," I pointed out to the girls.

"Monica!" Olivia exclaimed.

"That poor child could hardly get through a sentence without breaking down. There's no way she did it!" Cassandra scoffed.

"Guilty people cry too. They do it all the time on *Cold Case*," Olivia acknowledged with authority in her voice.

"Oh good grief, Olivia! You and your television shows," Cassandra declared and threw up her hands in exasperation.

"Look, she ate with her, stood with her on the sidelines, and she had opportunity. She was going to a therapist because as much as she loved her sister, she said she was unhappy. She lost who she was and what she wanted. Maybe she just cracked!" Olivia assumed.

"I don't know what to think. The Monica I knew twenty years ago wouldn't be capable of murder but people change. Maybe she figured she couldn't quit working for Katherine and was desperate. As much as I love Monica, I can't rule her out as a suspect," I admitted.

I felt awful for suspecting her, but Olivia was right! She had motive, her alibi was Katherine, and it was the classic *Cinderella* story of the oppressed sister being overlooked and treated poorly.

"I'll call Carl to bring the car around," Cassandra said and pulled her phone from her hand bag.

We rose together and headed toward the entrance of the Crescent Hotel. Maybe our trip to Ford Stadium would uncover some clues.

Chapter Fourteen

We were all quiet during the short drive to the SMU campus.

"I just can't wrap my brain around Monica doing something like that," Leslie thought out loud and frowned. "Poisoning is so violent. The Monica I knew wasn't violent," she said.

"Maybe her therapist could shed some light on her mental stability," Cassandra suggested.

"No way! The patient doctor confidentiality oath prevents her therapist from talking even with the police," Olivia stated in a robotic tone.

"Okay, I'm cutting you off from the legal shows!" Cassandra scoffed.

"Look, Cassandra. Would it change your mind about Monica if you found out she was Katherine's beneficiary? She mentioned there was no other family, so more than likely she was the sole beneficiary since Katherine had no children and had never been married," Olivia reminded her. "Amelia, you need to call Shane and find out what he learned from the police."

"I will after our visit to the campus. I want to get there before the maintenance crew leaves for the day," I said.

Carl pulled the town car up to the ticket window and we all piled out onto the sidewalk.

"This is the main entrance gate to the stadium. I hope it's open," I said as I pushed against the metal gate. "Drats! It's locked!"

"Where is the delivery area for the stadium? That's where we'll find an open gate," Olivia simply stated.

"Who are you? Cagney or Lacey?" Cassandra ribbed her. "I had no idea you were such a good investigator!"

"Cassandra, give me a little credit," she sighed and lightly punched her arm.

"Ouch, Olivia. You pack a mean punch!" Cassandra whined through her nose, rubbing her sore arm.

"Looks like you were right, Liv! The delivery gate is open," I pointed out.

No one was in sight, so we just let ourselves in. The driveway opened up onto the field. I felt so small and insignificant as I walked toward the sideline and looked at the towering stadium walls and the rows of seats all around us. We could see the skybox from this vantage point.

"We were right up there," I said pointing up towards the skybox.

"And Katherine stood right here at the fifty yard line," Olivia recalled and placed her feet on the painted white hatch marks on the grass. "She walked straight out," she said holding her elbow to the side pretending to be escorted by President Turner. "She stood here while he announced the award and then . . . "

"He placed the tiara on her head," Cassandra cut in, squarely placing an imaginary tiara on Olivia's head.

"She turned, walked to her right, I'm waving, I'm waving . . . " Olivia motioned looking up and smiling at the skybox.

"And then she grabbed her throat, choking. And then she fell on her knees," Cassandra finished.

"Yes and then, the paramedics rushed in from over there," Leslie said pointing to the tarmac. "They checked Katherine, put her on the gurney and rushed her to the hospital," she recalled.

"Okay, we're missing something. What are we missing?" I wracked my brain, trying to recall a key clue. Something wasn't right. I just couldn't figure out what it was. Just then my cell phone rang. It was Shane.

"Hello, Shane. How did it go with Detective Lincoln?" I asked hopefully.

"Well, that's what I wanted to talk with you about. Where are you, Amelia?" he asked.

"I'm at the football stadium on campus," I replied. Suddenly, I realized what wasn't adding up! "Shane, do you still have this morning's paper?" I blurted.

"Yeah, I brought it with me. Why do you ask, Amelia?"

"I want you to look at Katherine's picture and tell me what you see," I told him.

"I don't understand!" Shane complained.

"Please, honey. Just describe to me what you see in the picture," I pleaded.

"A picture of Katherine on the gurney, her eyes are closed. She's wearing an oxygen mask. I still don't get it!" he protested.

"Is she wearing anything else?" I quickly interrupted him.

"Like what, clothes?" He definitely was confused.

"No. Like a tiara?" I reminded him, the excitement rising in my voice.

"No, no she's not! I still am not following you," he said.

"Shane, see if Detective Lincoln has her tiara listed with her personal effects," I requested.

"Okay. Want to tell me why?" he asked.

"Because she collapsed right after President Turner placed the tiara on her head. It could have been the vehicle for introducing the poison," I deduced.

"A tiara? Really Amelia?" he belittled me.

"Really, Shane. Just ask him and call me back when you find out. I'm going to ask the maintenance crew here if they found her tiara on the field. Call me right away!" I snapped and quickly hung up the phone. I turned toward Olivia.

Olivia screamed, "You're a genius, Amelia! If you're right, the poison entered her system when the tiara was placed on her head. It fits her symptoms and collapse!" She hugged me, impulsively. "Let's find out if maintenance did find it!"

The four of us traced our steps back to the tarmac and looked around for the maintenance office. Just then a worker in uniform with a name badge walked towards us.

"Can I help you ladies find your way around?" he offered.

"Yes, Dan, I think you can!" I said reading his name badge. "Were you here during Saturday's game?" I asked him hopefully.

"Yes M'am, I was. That sure was sad what happened to Miss Gold," he lamented.

"We are actually close friends of Katherine. We were her roommates when we were at SMU and we are helping her sister out with some of her personal effects," Leslie said as she tossed her long silky black hair over her shoulder. Dan seemed mesmerized with Leslie.

"Anything I can do to help!" he whispered and shyly cast his eyes down towards the ground. He looked back up at Leslie.

"Dan, did you find anything belonging to Katherine? Maybe a shoe, her purse . . . or maybe her tiara?" she said and gazed directly into Dan's eyes. Obviously, Leslie had practiced this move before.

"You know, you're the second person that's come by today asking about a tiara," he informed us.

"Someone else came by asking about Katherine's tiara?" Olivia asked astonished, her voice rising ever so slightly.

"A woman. She said she was with the Dallas police," he stated.

"Did she give you her name or show you her badge?" Olivia asked placing her hands on her hips.

"No. Not that I recall," Dan said.

"Did you find the tiara?" I asked him. I was holding my breath.

150

"Yeah. It was on the field and the referee found it and had it removed from the field before the second half started," he observed.

Okay, great! They found the tiara and now the police had it. I pulled out my phone to tell Shane the good news. He answered on the first ring.

"Shane. The police have the tiara. I just talked with a maintenance crew member," I shared with him.

"Amelia, I'm here with Detective Lincoln right now. They don't have the tiara," he informed me.

"Well, maybe the police woman who picked it up hasn't turned it into the department yet," I explained.

"What police woman?" Shane asked.

"I don't know her name, but she came out to pick up the tiara from Dan," I stammered.

"I'll speak to Lincoln and tell him what you found out," Shane muttered. The line went dead and I turned back to Dan and the three ladies.

"Dan. Where's the tiara now? Did you give it to the police woman?" I asked nervously.

"You know, the phone rang and I turned my back on her in the office to answer it. When I turned around, she was gone. I thought that was strange!" he remarked.

"Did you give her the tiara?" Olivia asked him getting agitated.

"No, I didn't give it to her!" Dan said defensively. "It should still be in the office."

"Take us to the office, right away!" I demanded and slung my handbag over my shoulder, following Dan as quickly as I could. My stomach sank and I felt slightly faint.

He directed us a short distance down the hall to a door marked "Maintenance Office." He opened the door and walked over to the main desk.

"Marge. These ladies are here to retrieve Katherine Gold's personal belongings," Dan informed her. "I'm just going to go get the tiara for them." An older woman with leathery skin turned her desk chair towards us and looked over her reading glasses.

"What tiara?" Marge asked Dan, a puzzled look on her craggy face.

"The large tiara sitting behind the desk," Dan said and began fumbling between the stacks of invoices and the outgoing mail bin. "It was right here this morning!" he yelled.

"I never saw it and I came in around ten o'clock this morning," Marge told him and got up from her chair to help assist in the search. "A tiara, you say?" she reiterated.

"Yes a BIG tiara. Like a Miss Universe type," Olivia told her. "Katherine was wearing it when she collapsed on the field."

"Such a shame, such a shame!" Marge empathized. "She was such a beautiful woman!"

"I can't find it, anywhere!" Dan turned towards Marge and shook his head in bewilderment. "I don't know what could have happened to it!" he said visibly frustrated.

"I have a pretty good idea," I told the group. "Just how long did you have your back turned to the police woman?" I asked Dan.

"Oh, maybe three minutes at the most. I just had to take a call and then radio a truck. Yeah, three minutes at the most," he remembered.

"Just long enough for her to come behind the desk, see the tiara and take it," I surmised.

"She said she was with the Dallas police department," he argued.

"And I'm Paris Hilton," Olivia said off handedly. "You always get the badge number and I.D., Dan," she reproved him.

"I . . . I . . . I didn't know, but I didn't give her the crown. She must have taken it," he stammered.

"What did she look like, this police woman?" I questioned Dan. I was getting the sinking feeling that she wasn't affiliated at all with the investigation and that we had just lost our key piece of evidence that would clear our names.

"She had dark brown hair, glasses, kind of medium height. She was wearing a black suit. That's about all I could tell you," he shrugged.

"If I didn't know better, that almost sounds like Monica Gold," Olivia said suspiciously.

"I'm calling Shane, right now!" I pulled out my phone and before I had a chance to dial, it rang.

"Shane, I need to talk to Detective Lincoln right away," I said as I spoke into the phone.

"I'm at your service," Detective Lincoln answered in a formal manner.

"Oh, I thought you were Shane!" I admitted placed my hand on my chest, embarrassed by my mistake.

"Shane told me you are at the campus talking with a maintenance person who said one of our female officers was out there today," Detective Lincoln acknowledged.

"Yes, that's right," I agreed.

"Did he get her name because I didn't authorize anyone to pick up Miss Gold's belongings at the stadium? Furthermore, we don't have a female officer working this case," he informed me.

That's what I was afraid of. There was no police woman. Dan had been duped, hook, line and sinker. The evidence was gone, vanished. And we were still suspects.

"Come on in, Amelia. I think we need to talk," Lincoln requested.

"Sure. Let me call my attorney and I will be right over," I told him.

Could this day get any worse? I thought.

153

Chapter Fifteen

Mr. Simpson met me at the police headquarters. I sent Cassandra, Olivia and Leslie back to the Adolphus Hotel to relax and have some down time. There was nothing they could really do to help me at this point.

Cassandra reassured me that she would call and check on Sarah and that maybe all of us could get together for some dinner when I was finished with Detective Lincoln. I hoped I wouldn't be having my dinner in "Cell Block-D" tonight wearing an orange jumpsuit.

"Amelia. Don't answer any questions without my consent," Mr. Simpson implored. "Let's find out exactly what Detective Lincoln has as evidence before we get upset, okay!" He said and patted my arm as we were ushered into the same cold, sterile room with the same metal table and chairs. Mr. Simpson pulled one out for me and I sat down, waiting to hear my fate. He sat next to me and opened his leather briefcase, taking out a yellow legal pad and some notes.

"Mrs. Spencer, Mr. Simpson," Detective Lincoln said as he came in the room and shut the door behind him. "Your husband tells me you have an interesting theory about what happened to Miss Gold. I would like to hear it," he requested. He pulled out the chair directly across from me and sat down.

I looked over at Mr. Simpson and he nodded his approval.

"I think Katherine was poisoned by someone who delivered the toxin in her tiara," I said.

"This sounds more like a bad copycat of the movie, *Miss Congeniality* to me." He laughed and continued. "And conveniently, the tiara is nowhere to be found. So, I suppose that lets you off the hook," he said sarcastically.

"Well, maybe instead of questioning me, you should be looking for this woman who is impersonating a Dallas police officer. She knew that the tiara was a valuable piece of evidence and took the risk of going back to retrieve it!" I retorted.

"You got any other theories up your sleeve, *Kojak?*" He belittled me and then began laughing at his own joke. Gosh, there's nothing more that I despise than a smart aleck jerk! Detective Lincoln definitely fit the bill!

"Have you spoken with Monica Gold recently?" I asked him, leaning towards him.

"We spoke yesterday. Why?" he snapped.

"Katherine had a lot of enemies from what I gathered from Monica," I countered.

"Yes, I have talked with the F.B.I. about her disturbed fan mail," he commented.

"Did she tell you about the Italian photographer? Or the Bronsons?" I hinted.

"We are locating the photographer right now. We were able to identify him. Who are the Bronsons?" he asked surprised.

"Bo Bronson was Katherine's very married co-star whom she began an affair with a few months back," I disclosed to him.

"I thought she was seeing that Conrad kid," Lincoln admitted and scratched his head. Obviously, Detective Lincoln had not been keeping up with the celebrity gossip.

"That's been over for a while. She broke up with Bo to start seeing Conrad, but not before his wife found out and got her fired from the soap. Apparently she is related to the executive producer," I told him. I was enjoying filling him on for a change.

"Well, from what I gathered, Katherine dated married men as a hobby. So, what's the big deal about this Bronson fella?" He said, though I knew he was obviously interested.

"Bo had begun following her. He even was arrested for assault after attacking Conrad at a restaurant. There was an order of protection against him," I recited.

"You've been doing your homework, *Columbo*. That still doesn't let you and your friends off the hook," he said and smiled slyly from the left corner of his mouth.

"Are you charging my client with anything at this time, Detective?" Mr. Simpson demanded. "If not, I am requesting you to stop throwing around your false accusations!"

"Your client had motive, and was seen arguing with the victim shortly before her death," he reminded Mr. Simpson.

"There were a lot more people interested in hurting Katherine other than me," I reminded him.

"Like who, *Sherlock Holmes?*" I could tell he was trying to badger me.

"Like Bo Bronson who was in the middle of a nasty custody fight and didn't like Katherine two timing him with Conrad. Let's not forget the Italian photographer who was yelling ugly names at her or the woman who took the tiara from the maintenance office this morning. She could very well be your killer!" I retorted.

"Your old boyfriend, Jett would be another possibility," he redirected.

"Jett had nothing to do with this. If you are interested in looking up alibis for everyone that either lost a boyfriend to Katherine or who slept with Katherine, you would have to question just about every male who was at our class reunion cocktail reception Friday night!" I quipped.

"Yes, we have been interviewing quite a few of your classmates. They say that you practically dropped out of sight after Katherine's little affair with Jett," he said leaned back in his chair. He flexed his arms behind his head, a cocky smirk across his face. He was enjoying this! Boy, he was trying to get under my skin, but I was not about to give him the satisfaction.

"That's enough. If you're done, Detective Lincoln, my client and I will be leaving." Mr. Simpson interjected. He opened his briefcase and began packing his notes.

"Look, Detective Lincoln. I didn't do it. Though Katherine had her flaws, I loved her like a sister," I admitted.

"Even sisters can kill," he said smugly and looked me directly in the eyes.

Was he hinting to me that Monica Gold was a suspect? My first inclination was to believe that she was innocent. My opinion was based entirely on the Monica I knew from twenty years ago. My first knee jerk reaction would be to defend her. I had to keep reminding myself that I didn't know her as an adult and there were obvious problems between Katherine and her sister, enough so that she was seeing a therapist on a regular basis. She also matched the description Dan, the maintenance worker, had given us of the woman who impersonated a police officer. I decided to keep all my suspicions under my hat for right now. I didn't want to implicate her until I had dug a little deeper.

"Yes, that's true. But speaking of sisters, I suggest you talk to Monica Gold again. She mentioned Katherine had some appointments that she kept quiet from Monica who was her personal assistant. She can also tell you more about Bo and Sheila Bronson. Maybe you should see if they were in town over the weekend," I contended.

I got up and grabbed my purse. I was tired of being treated like a criminal, tired of Detective Lincoln wasting valuable time when he should be looking for the REAL murderer, and tired mentally.

"Mr. Simpson, please remind your client not to leave town until we are finished with this investigation," Detective Lincoln said while he pushed in his chair. He was becoming quite annoying.

"I have two children and a business to run back in Tennessee. I need to get back home as soon as possible. I have already extended my trip to be available to answer your questions," I complained.

Business. My business! I should be packing up the tea room this week! The closing was set for next Friday. I had a lot of work ahead of me, not to mention Charlie's football practices and just being there to help Emma and Charlie with their homework and daily activities. My life had literally been put on hold the moment Katherine Gold had died.

"Please remind your client that I can hold her for up to seventy-two hours without charging her with a crime. Her cooperation would be a good show of faith to the court," he intimated and quickly exited. I stood there with my mouth hanging open.

"Can he do that?" I asked shocked at the thought of being held that long.

"Yes, he can, and yes, he will, if you do not cooperate fully. I suggested to Shane that you may be here a few more days. It would be best to make arrangements for the care of the children," Simpson recommended as he adjusted his bowtie and grabbed his briefcase from the cold metal table.

"Amelia," he said as we exited the room. "Don't give up hope. This will be over with soon. The police are just doing their job," he said.

"Doing their job? Doing their job? I don't think harassing me instead of looking for this police woman imposter is doing their job. I practically gave that man a hand written list of who's who and all he can do is make condescending remarks and threaten to hold me!" I shouted.

"I'm sure Detective Lincoln is already following some of your leads. Cooperation goes a long way with the Texas courts," he explained.

I knew that the sooner things wrapped up here, the sooner I could get back to Dogwood Cove and back to my kids and my life. I had to find that tiara and figure out who had killed Katherine. I would have to keep digging for leads.

"Amelia, sweetheart," Shane said and hugged me as I walked out of the interview room. "Did everything go okay, Thomas?" he asked.

"I assured Amelia that the more she cooperates with the Dallas police, the sooner she can go home. Shane, Amelia, I will remain in town until this matter is resolved," he stated and extended his hand to Shane. He gave him a firm handshake and patted me on the arm.

"Get some rest, Amelia," Mr. Simpson said and headed out the door.

"Yes, rest. That's why I'm here. My lady, your chariot awaits!" Shane announced made a sweeping motion with his arm and quickly opened the front door. Carl and the town car were waiting and as I sank into the soft leather seats, I felt some of the tension of the day melt away.

"Shane, you need to go back home. The kids need one of us there and we have a lot going on with the closing this next week," I objected.

"Not another word, Amelia. You and I are going to have a nice relaxing dinner and we are not going to talk about anything unpleasant. You need to unwind and relax and I am here to make sure you do!" he insisted and gave me a kiss on the cheek and squeezed my hand for emphasis.

"Where's everyone?" I asked.

"Carl dropped the ladies off at The Galleria Mall for some shopping about an hour ago. I'm sure it will be a while before they are done," he predicted.

"Is Sarah with them?" I inquired.

"Yes. They picked her up along the way and Monica is staying in for the night at the hotel. Everyone is occupied and happy. Now it's your turn!" he decreed.

"Shane, I miss the kids so very much! I wish I was home. I would give both of them the biggest hugs and never let them go! This has become a nightmare," I remarked. I looked out the town car window as the Dallas skyline came into view.

"Speaking of the kids, Aunt Alice is having a ball with them and they both want you to call them right away." He pulled his cell phone from his belt holster and dialed our home number.

"Hello, Charlie?" I squealed.

"Mom! I'm so glad you called. When are you coming home?" Charlie said with a tinge of sadness in his voice.

"Soon, baby. Real soon! How's football going?" I asked.

"I threw two touch downs yesterday! It was so awesome because the field was muddy and we were covered in mud. It was so much fun! John Holston skidded halfway across the field when he caught my pass," he recounted.

I could just picture the dirty uniform and cleats waiting for me when I got home. I could also picture Charlie's freckled face splattered with mud.

"Have you finished your homework for school tomorrow?" I gently reminded him.

"Yep! I'm helping Aunt Alice make oatmeal raisin cookies. I think these are going to be my new favorite!" he predicted.

I laughed at the thought of my kitchen at home bustling with the activity of baking cookies and the wonderful aromas filling the house.

"Did you finish your library book?" I asked him.

"I'm working on it. I have to take a test on it tomorrow," he blurted.

"Get it done, okay! And don't skip to the last chapter and read the ending!" I chided him. I knew my son well enough to know that he often tried short cuts when he had other things he would rather be doing like baking cookies and hanging out in the kitchen with Aunt Alice.

"I love you, Mom! Come home soon, okay?" he pleaded.

"I love you, too Charlie! I'll be home as soon as I can. Is Emma nearby?" I requested.

"I'm right here, Mom!" Emma piped up.

"Hey, Emma, sweetheart!" Gosh it was so good to hear her voice. "How is everything going?" I asked.

"Good, good! We miss you, though," she reminded me. That was Emma, always so thoughtful.

"Not as much as I miss you guys! Hey, are you getting help with your homework?" I stressed.

"I've got it covered. Nathan has been coming over to help me study," Emma said.

"Nathan Johnson?" I asked. Oh, no. I needed to get home to keep an eye on this situation.

"Yes, that Nathan. Don't worry, Mom. Aunt Alice is making us study in the kitchen. She feeds Nathan dinner and he helps look over my work. He's the smartest kid in my class," she reassured me.

"Yeah and probably the cutest, too!" I teased her.

"Mom. I don't like him like that. We're just friends. Gosh!" she objected.

"Yeah, and I remember being just friends with your Dad, too," I joked.

"When are you coming home?" She asked quickly changing the subject.

"Hopefully soon. How's Aunt Alice doing?" I wondered.

"Great! She's a lot of fun. Don't worry, I already washed Charlie's football uniform," Emma informed me.

Wow, she was really becoming quite responsible.

"Thanks, Emma. You really are something else. I'm so proud of you!" I rejoiced.

"Why, because I can do a load of laundry?" she said sarcastically.

"No, because you did it without being asked. There's a difference!" I insisted.

"I know, I know! I'm special, right?" She was laughing now.

"You know it, sweetie," I agreed. Gosh I missed that sweet face and bright smile.

"Can you put Aunt Alice on the phone?" I asked Emma.

"Sure. Here's she is. Love you, Mom!"

"Love you too, Emma. I miss you!" I told her and blew her a kiss over the phone.

"Hello, Amelia!" Aunt Alice called out in a sing song rhythm.

"Thank you so much for staying longer, Aunt Alice." I was so glad to know she was there giving the kids daily stability.

"There's nowhere else I would rather be. How are you holding up, dear?" she asked in her most maternal tone.

"I'm glad Shane is with me, but I think he needs to be home with the kids," I admitted.

"We are holding down the fort. You just worry about you. I'm enjoying the tea room and the kids. It's been fun for me. So you take care of what you need to and take your time. I have no plans until Christmas," she maintained. She was so reassuring and so generous with her time. Thank goodness for Aunt Alice.

"Thank you, Aunt Alice! You are a lifesaver! Hopefully, I will be home before Christmas," I joked.

"You will be home soon, sweetheart, don't you worry," Alice reaffirmed.

"Thank you, Aunt Alice!"

"I'll save you some oatmeal raisin cookies," she promised.

"I doubt there will be any left after Charlie starts eating them," I laughed and smiled at the thought of Charlie putting his hand in the cookie jar.

"He reminds me of Shane so much. Shane had quite an appetite at that age," she reminisced.

"He still does," I told her and pictured Shane and Aunt Alice baking cookies when he was a young boy. He had the same freckled angelic face and beaming smile as Charlie. They were two peas in a pod.

"Amelia, we're here!" Shane prompted and I looked around, unaware that we had arrived at The Mansion on Turtle Creek, our dinner destination.

"Aunt Alice, I'm going to have to go, but I will call in the morning. Thank you so much again," I stressed.

"You and Shane take care and we are doing fine. I will keep you in my prayers," Aunt Alice said.

"Thank you, Aunt Alice," I said as we hung up. Shane came around to open my door. I needed some quiet time alone with Shane. I would put off worrying about everything until tomorrow.

Chapter Sixteen

While everyone slept in, Shane and I stole a quiet moment to share a pot of coffee and some warm cinnamon rolls.

"What did you and Lincoln talk about yesterday?" I asked him as I felt the sun's morning rays on my fair Irish skin. I pulled on my cable knit sweater to prevent too much of a good thing. My dermatologist would be happy with me.

"Don't you want to wait a bit before we plunge into all this, this morning?" Shane suggested.

"Look, we agreed last night not to talk about it, but that was last night. If I am going to clear my name and get home to my family, I need to figure all this out. The police don't seem to be doing such a hot job of it right now," I asserted.

"The police know more than you realize. In fact, the toxicology report should be in today and Lincoln promised to phone Thomas with the specifics on the poison that killed Katherine," Shane said.

"Really? He's sharing information?" I jeered. I couldn't believe Lincoln would discuss the case with a suspect.

"I think after you called with your lead on the phony police woman yesterday, he knows that you are actually trying to help," Shane affirmed.

"He didn't act like he appreciated my help yesterday. If anything, he treated me like I was fantasizing about the tiara since it conveniently disappeared," I snapped and took a big bite out of my cinnamon roll, taking my frustration out on it.

"Cassandra was going to talk yesterday with her L.A. connections at 'The Rich & The Lost' to see if anyone knew where Sheila and Bo Bronson have been over the last few days," Shane reminded me, picking up the newspaper to read the morning headlines.

"Well, let's not wake her up too early. L.A. people are still asleep on Pacific time," I urged.

"It looks like we won't need to bother Cassandra with that phone call," Shane handed the front page to me. In big bold letters the headlines screamed, "Bronson Kills Wife in Murder Suicide Sunday."

"Shane, oh, my gosh! How horrible!" I covered my mouth in astonishment and continued reading the article out loud.

I proceeded to read the rest of the story. "The police said they received a 911 call from one of the children that their Mom and Dad were fighting and that Bo Bronson had entered the home with a rifle. Oh, Shane! How could he do that with the children in the home?" I pleaded.

"He obviously was very disturbed. Those poor kids," Shane remarked and shook his head in amazed silence.

"Monica told us he had been following Katherine and had even hacked into her cell phone calendar and assaulted Conrad. He sounds like he was loose cannon," I shared with him.

"When did all this happen?" Shane asked, crossing over to the railing, leaning his forearms on the edge.

"A couple of months ago. She had an order of protection issued against him," I answered.

"Shane, the article says that Sheila and Bo had a divorce hearing on Friday and that full custody had been awarded to Sheila. Bo had to been issued a contempt of court charge for disorderly conduct during the hearing and spent twenty-four hours in jail," I recited. I kept scanning the article for more details.

"So that clearly establishes that the Bronson's were nowhere near Dallas on Saturday if they had a hearing Friday and the murder suicide was Sunday," Shane concluded.

"I guess there is always a possibility, but very slim," I agreed.

"Gosh, first Katherine. Now Bo Bronson. This is not looking good for 'The Rich & The Lost.' They've had two major stars die in one weekend," he said.

"Good for ratings, though," Cassandra said as she walked out onto the terrace. She was wearing a baby blue pant suit today and looked every bit the part of a Reynolds's executive.

"I guess you heard, then?" Shane asked as he walked over to the coffee pot to pour a second cup.

"Yeah, it's all over TV this morning. They already are doing a special program linking Bo and Katherine's deaths. Their relationship was very public. This is just what the viewers eat up," Cassandra groaned. She poured herself a cup of coffee and helped herself to a cinnamon roll.

"Mmm. These are good! Quick, let's eat them before Olivia wakes up!" she joked.

"Did you'll have a productive shopping trip at The Galleria Mall?" I asked.

"Olivia has turned into a shop-a-holic. I think I have created a monster!" Cassandra admitted.

"What do you mean?" Shane asked.

"She went crazy in the Prada store. I practically had to tear her away when they announced the mall was closing," she recounted and wiped her mouth on a napkin. She smiled at us both.

"Are you talking about *Our Olivia*, the one who would rather be 'dead than wear designer'?" Shane quoted.

"Cassandra has helped Olivia tap into her inner diva," I told him. "She is realizing there's more to life than mucking stalls and baling hay."

"Hey, I resent that!" Olivia said and marched out onto the terrace. I thought I smelled cinnamon rolls!" she exclaimed. She picked up a plate and helped herself to two.

"Good morning, Miss Olivia," Shane greeted her and watched Olivia inhale her breakfast. "Did you sleep well?"

"Yes, but someone was talking in their sleep last night," she complained.

"Who?" I asked her.

"Leslie. Something was obviously bothering her. She kept saying she was sorry over and over again," she said.

"Hmm. I wonder what that's all about," I said moving over to make room for Olivia.

"Did you hear the news this morning?" Cassandra asked Olivia.

"What? What happened?" Olivia demanded.

"Bo Bronson murdered his wife and then shot himself Sunday morning," Cassandra stated matter-of-factly moving next to Olivia.

"Oh, my gosh! Why would he do that?" Olivia exploded.

"I think he was a very unstable person, that's why," I said to Olivia.

"Do you think maybe he was the one sending Katherine those freaky fan letters?" she speculated taking another bite.

"You know, that's a thought. He definitely was disturbed enough and they started a few months ago about the time she ended it with him," I agreed with her. "I think I should give Detective Lincoln a call."

"No need, Amelia. He's here," Sarah announced and escorted him to the terrace.

"Detective Lincoln," Shane greeted him and shook his hand.

"What brings you out so bright and early this October morning? Continuing your witch hunt?" Olivia said snidely.

"Amelia, don't say a word until I call Thomas over here," Cassandra warned. She pulled out her cell phone and began dialing his number.

"That won't be necessary. I'm not here to question Amelia," Lincoln reassured us.

"Don't believe a word he says, Amelia!" Olivia snarled at him.

"You can call off the firing squad," he said as he shot Olivia a nasty look. "I'm here to share information," he offered.

"Share information with him and you'll be sharing a cell with Big Bertha," Olivia mumbled loudly enough for all of us to hear.

"Olivia. It's okay." Shane told her. "Detective Lincoln is just as interested as we are to catch Katherine's killer," he told her.

"Why don't we step inside where it's nice and air conditioned," I suggested. It was getting hot out on the terrace or maybe just being around Detective Lincoln got my blood pressure boiling. More than likely it was a combination of the two.

We all gathered around the large glass dining room table and waited for Lincoln to speak.

"So, what do we owe the pleasure of your company?" Olivia retorted.

Lincoln ignored Olivia and addressed the rest of us.

"You're going to hear it on the news in the next day or so. We've pinpointed the type of toxin in Miss Gold's blood stream," Lincoln said.

"What was it?" Shane asked first.

"Tetradoxin. It is a powerful venom that causes neuromuscular paralysis. Within three minutes, respiratory failure occurs," he reported.

"That would explain why she grabbed her throat and made the universal choking sign," Sarah said, her eyes wide in alarm.

"Tetradoxin. I've never heard of it? Where is it found?" I asked Lincoln.

"It is venom from a rare type of octopus," Lincoln replied.

"Are you serious? An octopus? I've never heard of an octopus being venomous other than the giant squid from *20,000 Leagues*

168

Under the Sea! To this day, I still can't eat calamari!" Olivia exclaimed.

"Olivia, you are a nut job!" Cassandra mused. "Detective, please excuse my good friend here. Continue!"

"The venom is from a specific octopus, the blue ringed octopus from Australia. One blue ringed octopus, though only the size of a golf ball, has enough venom to kill twenty-six adult men," Lincoln explained.

"How horrible," Sarah said gasping. "Remind me not to go snorkeling in Australia."

"Your theory, Amelia, about the tiara is probably correct. The coroner found some small puncture wounds on Miss Gold's scalp that matched the combs from the tiara. He believes that is how the venom was introduced to her blood stream. The scalp is an extremely vascular area and death would have happened in a matter of minutes," Lincoln emphasized.

"So, why didn't President Turner get sick from the tiara as well?" I asked Lincoln. "He was the one who placed it on her head," I recalled.

"He was lucky, but we have a theory that the combs that were fixed on either side of the tiara had sharp teeth that had been dipped in the venom. We're reviewing all of the NBC video footage of President Turner placing the crown on Katherine's head to see if that theory is feasible. Without the actual crown, we have no way of knowing for sure," he disclosed to us.

"President Turner was a lucky man that he didn't somehow get that on him!" Sarah remarked.

" You're right, he was lucky. The crown was sitting on top of a pillow for the presentation, so he didn't seem to have contact with the comb's teeth," Lincoln told Sarah.

"Could he have been a target as well, since this venom is so fatal?" I asked him.

"It's possible. We're not ruling that out. But most likely he just would have been collateral damage if he had been exposed.

Katherine was definitely the target since she would be the recipient of the tiara," he continued.

"Who knew she would be crowned?" Olivia asked the group of us.

"I heard it was Katherine's idea to be crowned since she was a past homecoming queen. Didn't Monica say something about that?" Cassandra offered.

"No, it wasn't Monica. Who was it?" I wondered. I tried to remember where I had heard that Katherine was receiving a crown. Something Olivia had said about the movie *Carrie* was coming back to me. Oh, well. I would think about that tidbit later.

"But, we still don't know who the mysterious woman was who showed up at the maintenance office," Cassandra said.

"After we talked with Amelia, we interviewed the maintenance office staff and had a sketch artist work up a drawing. Unfortunately, our main witness had his back to her most of the time, so we aren't very confident in how accurate it is," Lincoln shared with us.

He pulled out a black and white sketch of a woman with large glasses and a non-descript face. She looked to be about forty with brown eyes and medium length brown hair.

"She looks like the woman who waited on me at the perfume counter at Estee Lauder yesterday and about every other woman I saw at the mall," Cassandra stated.

"Yeah. That's what I was afraid of. Our witness wasn't very attentive to details," Lincoln said.

"What's going on?" Leslie asked as she entered the room. She was wearing her hair pulled back in a simple pony tail and had on dark dress jeans and a smart ruffled green blouse. Her makeup hardly covered the dark circles under her eyes.

"Miss Lane," Detective Lincoln addressed her as he stood up.

"Here, Leslie. Have a seat and I'll grab you some coffee and some breakfast, if Olivia left any cinnamon rolls for the rest of us," Sarah quipped. "Detective, may I get you some coffee and a roll as well?"

"Coffee will be fine. Thank you," he replied.

"Leslie. It's been a busy morning already. Detective Lincoln has told us the poison that killed Katherine was from a rare octopus," I announced to Leslie.

"What? How is that possible?" she asked as she stirred sweetener into her coffee.

"The combs of her crown were dipped in the octopus venom which entered her blood stream rather quickly," Lincoln told her.

"How horrible. Poor Katherine!" she said stunned. "Why would someone do that to her?" she asked.

"That was my next question," Lincoln said. "You mentioned Miss Gold's sister had spoken with you. Have you been in contact with her lately?" he asked us.

"Not since yesterday," Sarah said alarmed. "I left her around two o'clock in the afternoon. She said she wanted to take a nap and she needed some time alone."

"She's not at her hotel," Lincoln said and took a sip of his coffee. He placed it down and continued. "Housekeeping said her things were still there, but her bed had not been slept in. Any idea where she could have gone?"

"Oh, no! I knew I shouldn't have left her alone!" Sarah cried, panic rising in her voice. "She was so upset yesterday. She said something about being the only one who understood Katherine."

"I'm sure she is probably busy making Katherine's final arrangements," Cassandra offered, trying to ease Sarah's fears.

"Well, we've run a trace on her cell phone and her GPS monitor is not working. We have no idea where she is," Lincoln reiterated. "I was hoping you could remember some place she used to hang out or someone she knew that she might be with."

"No. I can't think of any specific place, can you Leslie?" I said looking over at Leslie.

"No. She always hung out with us. She's not from Dallas, so she just visited occasionally," Leslie shared with the detective.

"Well, if you hear from her, I need to speak to her immediately," he demanded.

"I guess you heard about the Bronsons this morning? You can cross them off you list of suspects," I told him.

"That is what I wanted to discuss with Monica. The F.B.I. has linked Sheila Bronson's fingerprints to the threatening mail Katherine was receiving," he informed us.

"Oh, my gosh! She really must have hated her!" Sarah declared.

"So Bo wasn't the only one who was crazy, then," Shane concluded fidgeting in his chair. "This has been a morning of revelations."

"So, you're still looking for the mystery woman from the sketch and the Italian photographer who was yelling threats at Katherine, right?" I asked the detective.

Lincoln answered, "Yes. I've ruled out your old buddy, Jett. He was sitting with a group of fraternity brothers during the half-time show and had been with them most of the morning. His alibi is solid." He gave me a sideways glance as he shared this good news.

"I never thought he was capable of hurting Katherine. He stands to lose too much right now," I told him.

"Well, I need to speak to Monica right away. If you hear from her, please call me," he requested.

"Of course, yes, right away!" Shane said and stood up from the table.

"Ladies, if you'll excuse me. Olivia," he said and nodded his head in her direction. "A pleasure as always." He walked out of the suite and the door shut loudly behind him.

"Gosh that man gives me the creeps!" Olivia said rubbing her arms like she had felt a chill.

"More like goose bumps, I think!" Cassandra shot at her. "If I didn't know better, I think Detective Lincoln has found himself a woman strong enough to spar with," she teased.

"Oh, Cassandra! I wouldn't have anything to do with him if he were the last man on the planet," she protested.

"I think thou dost protest too much!" Cassandra informed Olivia. "He definitely made a point of saying goodbye to you," she noted.

"Yeah, I noticed that too!" Sarah joined in. She was wearing a pair of black pencil leg Capri pants with black flats and a black scoop neck sweater reminiscent of Audrey Hepburn. She looked cute as a button.

"Stay out of this, Sarah," Olivia warned.

"Well, he did make a point of saying your name," she defended her opinion.

"Oh, gosh! Here we go again," Shane said and sighed.

"Where's Leslie?" I asked the girls gathered around the table playfully teasing each other.

"I think she's out on the terrace," Sarah said.

I walked over to the French doors and saw Leslie standing with her hands on the railing, her shoulders moving up and down as though she was quietly crying. I had detected something had been bothering Leslie the last few days. Maybe she would share with me what it was and why she had been saying she was sorry in her sleep last night.

"Leslie, honey. Are you okay?" I asked and walked out to stand beside her. She was looking across to the Dallas skyline as tears were streaming down her face. Something was terribly wrong with Leslie! I put my arms around her and held her while she sobbed, wracked with pain.

"There's something I never told you," she said between gulps of air. "You know when you left for England, I stayed behind for the summer at the apartment," she paused and swallowed.

"Yes," I answered.

"Well, I don't know how to say this, but just to say it and get it out," she cried and dabbed her eyes.

"Get what out?" I asked. What could be so terrible?

"Katherine found out she was pregnant two weeks after you left for London." She looked up at me and placed her hands on my shoulders. "The baby may have been Jett's."

"Baby? What baby?" Was I hearing this correctly? Katherine had been pregnant? I didn't remember hearing anything about a baby!

Leslie looked me right in the eye and spoke slowly. "Katherine had a baby while you were away in London. She found out she was pregnant right after graduation. No one else knew about it and I didn't want to add to your pain after your broken engagement," she confessed.

I turned to face the balcony and placed both my hands on the railing. Katherine had been pregnant. Jett could be the father. I gripped the rail until my knuckles turned white.

"Amelia. Are you okay?" Leslie's concern was genuine and she rubbed her hand gently up and down the middle of my back.

"Wow. I wasn't expecting to hear that," I told her as I looked out over the Dallas skyline. "Does Jett know?" I asked.

"I don't know, honey. Katherine and I were not on speaking terms when she left. She moved back West with an aunt and it wasn't too long after that she was on 'The Rich and the Lost,' " Leslie finished and continued to cry softly.

I shook my head, pulled a tissue from my pocket and dabbed my eyes. "I didn't know things could even get much worse than they already were," I told her. "What happened to the baby? Did she have it?" I wondered.

Leslie shrugged her shoulders. "I don't know. I really don't know. Like I said, we didn't speak for a long time. Maybe Monica would know," she suggested.

Monica. Yes, Monica would know. And if Katherine had a child, that child needed to know that he or she had just lost their mother.

"We've got to get a hold of Monica right away and find out about the baby!" I shouted and grabbed Leslie's hand. We rushed inside to the living room of the suite.

"Amelia, sweetheart, are you okay?" Cassandra asked as she rose from the love seat.

"Can we take the town car back over to the Mansion on Turtle Creek?" I quickly asked her.

"Of course, of course! Is something wrong?" Cassandra questioned.

"Katherine was pregnant and Monica may be the only one who knows what happened to the baby," I told the group. "We've got to talk with Monica and find out what she knows," I said.

"When did this happen?" Olivia asked. "Did I miss something?"

"Pregnant? When?" Shane asked.

"Right after graduation," I told him as I gathered up my handbag.

"Right after she slept with Jett," Olivia surmised.

"Yes." Leslie said to the filled room. "I didn't tell Amelia. She was too hurt already," she explained.

"That was probably best, don't you think, Amelia?" Sarah said and walked over to me and put her arm around my shoulders in a show of compassion. Sarah—always the peacemaker.

"But, Monica is missing. The police are looking for her now!" Olivia exclaimed.

"Honey, the police are already looking for Monica. They probably have someone at the hotel waiting for her. What do you hope to gain by talking with her?" Shane asked as he sympathetically looked into my eyes.

"I'm thinking that child has a right to know what has happened to his or her mother. Think about Charlie and Emma." I looked into Shane's face as he nodded his head in agreement.

"This isn't about Jett," I looked around the room at the supportive faces of friends through the years, "This is about Katherine and her baby."

We were all dabbing our eyes and shaking our heads in agreement.

"Jett. What about Jett? Wouldn't he know if he were the father?" Olivia prompted the collective group of friends.

I looked to Leslie for affirmation.

"I don't know," she sighed. "I was so upset with Katherine, we didn't speak for years. She never told me that Jett was the father."

"Maybe Jett is still in town?" Sarah meekly piped up.

"Maybe. Let's call Detective Lincoln and see if he has a cell phone number or hotel since they were questioning Jett earlier," I said with strength. "He may be able to clear this up quickly!"

We all gathered up our handbags and coats and headed to the lobby where Carl was waiting patiently with the town car to take us to the Dallas Police Station.

"Does anyone else feel like a couple of White Castle hamburgers or maybe a Jack in the Box?" Olivia sheepishly asked as we piled into the limo.

"You are the only one I know who could eat at a time like this, Olivia Rivers!" Cassandra chastised and shook her head.

"Protein keeps the brain at tip top performance and that's what we need right now," she said defensively to Cassandra.

"I think you're right, Olivia," Shane said. "We should get something to eat before we talk with Jett. This might be a long day."

Shane's words could not have rung more true. This would be a long day. . . . and a day we would look back on and shudder!

Chapter Seventeen

After a quick lunch on the go, we arrived at the Dallas Police station. Shane had called Detective Lincoln on the way and shared with him the information that Katherine Gold may have had a child. Detective Lincoln was waiting in the lobby when we arrived and ushered us to a large conference room.

"Shane, ladies, have a seat. Olivia," he addressed her as he pulled out a chair for her gingerly and gestured for her to take a seat. Olivia thanked him and sat down, allowing Lincoln to scoot her chair towards the table. She looked up at Lincoln and smiled coyly.

Cassandra didn't miss the exchange and began tittering in her chair. She attempted to hide her laughter. She made eye contact with Olivia who glared at her.

"Well, this makes finding Monica Gold that much more significant," Detective Lincoln said as he crossed his arms and looked at the wipe-off board covered with diagrams and photos of the crime scene. "Is Jett Rollins the father?" he pointedly asked and glanced in my direction.

"I would have no way of knowing since I didn't speak to Jett or Katherine after I left for London," I told him matter-of-factly. "Leslie was never told who the father was of IF she had the baby. Katherine moved back West to stay with an aunt and shortly was hired by the network to do her soap," I concluded.

"Seems Jett should be able to clear this up," Lincoln said and sat on the edge of the table, closest to Olivia, his arms still in crossed in an authoritative manner. "I was able to reach him by cell phone and he's on his way now," Lincoln revealed.

There was a knock on the door and an officer opened it abruptly and escorted Jett into the room. All eyes were on him as he shook Lincoln's hand and took an empty chair next to Sarah.

"Jett, I'm Shane Spencer," Shane said as he extended his hand to Jett.

"Shane, nice to meet you," he said as he shook hands across the table. "Amelia," he greeted me as he sat back down, a strained expression on his face.

"Jett, I need to ask you some questions about your relationship with Katherine Gold," Lincoln said as he stood up and began pacing the crowded room. "Were you aware that Katherine found out she was pregnant shortly after graduation?" Lincoln inquired.

A hush fell across the room as all eyes focused on Jett and his reaction. I tried not to look at him.

His face registered total surprise and it took him a few moments to collect his thoughts.

"Pregnant, Katherine? No, I was not aware of that," Jett whispered and paused.

Lincoln cleared his throat and asked, "Could it be possible that you were the father?"

Jett's fists clenched and he looked down at the table. "I highly doubt it," he responded.

"Were you not intimately involved with Miss Gold around the time of her graduation?" Lincoln asked abruptly. He began pacing behind Jett's chair.

"Yes, I'm not denying that we were intimate, but just one time," Jett stated and looked out of the corner of his eyes in my direction. Shane held my hand under the table and gave it a gentle squeeze of support.

"It only takes one time to get pregnant with my mares last time I checked," Olivia accused Jett as she leaned across the table towards him. "And one time is all it takes to be a cheater!"

"Olivia! Please try to control yourself," Cassandra hissed under her breath.

"Well, if he had kept his pants zipped, we wouldn't even be having this discussion!" she snipped back at Cassandra.

"Katherine never told me about a pregnancy, but I am one hundred percent sure I could not be the father!" Jett exclaimed.

"And how do you know with such certainty?" Lincoln asked, both hands on the table looking Jett directly in the eye.

"My wife and I just went through infertility studies. When I said the twins were a miracle for us, that was not a slight exaggeration," Jett said and looked very uneasy. He swallowed hard.

"I found out that I was sterile. We had to use a sperm donor to conceive the twins," Jett revealed.

"Wow. This is better than a *Law and Order* Marathon," Olivia chuckled. "Sterile?"

"Show some compassion, Liv!" Sarah said and slapped her hand.

"Sorry, Jett. Tough break," Olivia said with sincere sympathy in her voice.

"Any idea who the father might be since Mr. Rollins has been ruled out?" Lincoln asked the group.

"Leslie? Do you have any ideas about who else she was seeing?" I asked.

"Like I said, we weren't on speaking terms after the, um, situation with Jett," Leslie said and crossed her arms. "It could have been anyone. She dated a lot of men," she added.

Jett spoke up. "I'm pretty sure I knew who Katherine was seeing . . . Carson Craig."

"Carson Craig? Are you sure?" I asked him in disbelief.

Carson Craig was the man about campus, the all-star football player and one of the most popular guys at SMU. I had never heard

Katherine mention him, but it wouldn't surprise me if they had hooked up at one time since they would almost be like a "Barbie and Ken" super couple with her golden hair and his muscular build.

"Did Carson attend the reunion?" Lincoln asked Jett.

"Yeah, he was at the Meadows Museum reception and the football game. We were fraternity brothers and a group of us had block seats at homecoming. He lives here in Dallas. It shouldn't be hard to look him up," Jett suggested.

"I'll have someone go pick him up now. Stay put, okay?" Lincoln said and slammed the door behind him.

There was an awkward silence in the room. No one knew quite what to say. For once I was glad Olivia didn't have a smart remark or quip.

Sarah was the first to speak. "Did you bring any pictures with you of the twins?" she gently asked Jett breaking the ice.

"Yes, I have some right here," he said and removed his wallet from the back pocket of his jeans. "This is Bonnie and the little guy on the left is Jacob," he shared with her. He seemed to be glad to have something to focus his attention on other than the interrogation from Detective Lincoln.

"Wow. They are beautiful, Jett. You are lucky!" Sarah smiled at him and handed back the photos. "And your wife? How long have you been married?" she asked.

"About ten years now. Laura's at home with the children. I really miss them," he said as he placed his wallet back. "Laura and the kids are everything to me," he confessed emphatically.

I gave Shane's hand another gentle squeeze. Everything had turned out for the best. I had my beautiful Emma and handsome Charlie. I was missing them so much right now. And I was blessed to have found such a wonderful man — the person with whom I was supposed to end up with. I knew that with one hundred percent certainty.

The door swung open abruptly and Lincoln strode in the room. Everyone looked up hopefully.

"Carson Craig is missing," Lincoln announced. "His wife Shelly said he never came home after the game Saturday. She says his phone keeps going directly to voicemail."

"I was with Carson in the parking lot," Jett said shaking his head. "He was getting his car keys out and we were saying our goodbyes. He seemed fine."

"Where were you parked?" Lincoln quickly asked.

"The campus parking garage, third level," Jett stated.

Lincoln left the room at a jog and the door slammed once again. This was becoming more and more bizarre. Monica was missing. Now Carson!

"First Monica, and now Carson, I should never have left Monica alone," Sarah said as tears began forming in the corner of her eyes. "Something bad has happened. If I had just been with her," she admonished herself.

"Then we might be looking for you too!" Olivia informed her. "Think about it Sarah! Someone killed Katherine. The probable father of Katherine's baby is missing along with her sister. Someone could have hurt you if you were in the way," Olivia reminded her.

"Do you think Monica is responsible for Carson's disappearance?" Shane asked me.

"No way. Monica was always a sweet girl!" I answered.

"No way would Monica do something like this, I agree with Amelia." Leslie said.

Lincoln returned a grave look on his face.

He said, "I ran Craig's license plates. His car is still in the campus parking garage. It looks like he never made it to his car," he said and walked over to Jett. "Did you see anyone or anything suspicious while you were saying good bye?"

Jett paused and began rubbing his hand across his chin reflectively. "No. No. Just the usual gang from the old days. Nothing out of the ordinary," Jett remarked.

"The gang from the old days? Who would that have been?" Lincoln wondered out loud.

"A bunch of us from homecoming," Jett responded. "Let's see. There was Ethan Tallent, Frank Dupree, Rachel Collins, Holly Smith, Alex Whittaker."

"Wait, wait Jett!" I exclaimed. "Back up. Did you say Holly Smith?"

"Yeah. Why?" Jett asked.

"Holly had that huge crush on Carson, remember?" I turned to Leslie. "She was almost weird about it. She wore his campaign pins all over her backpack when he was nominated for Homecoming King, remember?"

"Yeah. She was head over heels in love with him," Leslie agreed and nodded her head in affirmation.

"She drove everyone crazy running around campus with that bull horn screaming 'Carson for King!' I thought she might end up costing him some votes, she was so rabid about it," I told Detective Lincoln.

"Just like she's rabid about the sorority?" Cassandra pointed out. "She was very pushy Saturday about donations and bequeathing in wills."

"I did call her the 'Grim Reaper.' Maybe she's worse than we thought. Maybe she's not so harmless!" Olivia added.

"Did you see this Holly Smith with Carson Craig?" Lincoln asked Jett.

Jett paused and had a faraway look in his eyes. "Yeah. When we were all going our separate ways, she was pulling on his arm and saying something about Carson needing to walk her to her car. I didn't think anything of it. It's Holly. She's always been a bit of a pain in the neck," he added.

"Sounds like she's more than just a pain in the neck. She's a stalker!" Olivia blurted out.

"Where's this Holly Smith live?" Lincoln inquired of us.

"She lives out in Monterey, California. She's some kind of marine biologist, I think I remember reading in our sorority class notes," Leslie said.

"Leslie! Marine biologists would have access to marine animals such as blue ringed octopus!" I shouted and grabbed her arm. "I think we know who killed Katherine!"

"I knew she was creepy, but wow, she really is scary!" Olivia remarked.

"We've got to find Holly Smith and fast!" Lincoln yelled and flung the door open. "Rodriguez! Put out an A.P.B. on Holly Smith of Monterey, California, STAT! Lincoln shouted to his officer. Everyone began scurrying around the squad room.

"Oh, my goodness, Amelia! Do you really think Holly is capable of killing Katherine?" Sarah asked, obviously stunned. "She seemed to be so happy that the newspaper had Katherine on the front page Saturday," she remembered.

"Yes. She didn't seem to be jealous of her in the least. If anything, she seemed proud," Cassandra added.

"Yes, proud that our sorority was getting notoriety that our most famous member was on the front page of *The Dallas Morning News*. It's always been Gamma Phi first with Holly," I said as I began to realize what was unfolding in front of us.

"Everything in Holly's life has been Gamma Phi Beta," Leslie spoke up. "She took the presidency to heart. She's still very actively involved with the alumnae association."

"What would cause her to kill Katherine, though? Shane inquired. "This still is not making sense to me."

"I think with Katherine dead, her celebrity status would be elevated even more, like Marilyn Monroe," I surmised.

"More like Anna Nicole Smith," Olivia added.

"And Gamma Phi would have an 'infamous' celebrity member," Sarah said. "I think I get it."

"And," Cassandra said rising to her feet, "if she were really obsessed with Carson, she could get Katherine out of the way and have him all to herself."

"Leslie, do you think Holly found out about Carson and Katherine?" I asked as I turned towards Leslie.

"Like I said, I wasn't on speaking terms with Katherine and I am just now hearing about Carson and Katherine, but something did happen at the sorority house around graduation," she recalled.

"What? Tell us, Leslie!" Sarah encouraged her to quickly continue.

"I left our apartment after the 'incident' with Katherine and Jett. Sorry, Jett! But hey, it happened," Leslie paused and continued. "I stayed at the Gamma Phi House for the next week while I packed up my things in the apartment whenever Katherine wasn't around. I couldn't stand to stay there with what happened to Amelia. I remember during my stay at the sorority house that Holly was acting really weird," she recalled.

"How could you tell, Leslie?" Olivia asked. "She seems to be certifiable most of the time. By the way, anyone have some crackers or nuts or something?" Olivia asked.

Cassandra shot a look at Olivia. "Please continue Leslie," reprimanded her.

Leslie continued, "I should say that Holly had a melt-down one evening. We were all hanging out in the living room watching *Melrose Place* when I remember one of the pledges running downstairs saying Holly had locked herself in one of the bathroom stalls and was crying hysterically."

"What happened?" Sarah asked breathlessly.

"We went upstairs and she was sobbing, uncontrollably. She was ripping up pictures and flushing them down the toilet. I never saw who or what the pictures were of, but she was definitely upset," Leslie said.

Poor Holly. She had been a victim of Katherine as well. I imagine she found out about the relationship with Carson and just lost it, I was assuming.

"We had to get the house Mom to come up and talk with her. I thought we might have to call for help. She was really upset and was in there for hours, screaming and crying," Leslie told everyone.

"Leslie, did she ever say what happened?" I asked guessing she was heartbroken.

"All she said was that she had been such a fool to believe 'him,'" she repeated.

"Believe who?" We were all on pins and needles, waiting for Leslie's response.

"She never said. She was crying one minute and throwing things the next. She was like Dr. Jekyll and Mr. Hyde. It was frightening. We were all up most of the night feeling worried about her one minute and terrified the next that she was crazy!" Leslie testified.

"Wow. I thought I was the one having the adventures over in London," I said. "How bizarre!"

"Well, it fits the time frame of when Carson and Katherine were dating. They decided to call it quits a few days before graduation. Carson was drunk over at the frat house saying he was leaving for grad school and didn't need to be tied down to anyone," Jett confirmed.

"Do you think he knew she was pregnant?" I asked Jett.

"Carson's a pretty stand up guy. I can't imagine he would turn his back on Katherine if he knew. The way I understood it, she was leaving to audition in L.A. and he had plans to go to grad school at Chapel Hill," Jett responded.

Detective Lincoln interrupted suddenly, "We just got a break. We were able to track the G.P.S. on Monica Gold's phone to Harry Hines Boulevard. We're heading over there now." He slapped the doorframe twice in excitement.

"I don't want to sit here and wait. We need to follow them!" Sarah said and flung her thrift shop handbag over her arm. "Monica needs us!"

"Carl will be able to drive the town car fast and keep up. Come on!" Cassandra shouted and we all pushed our chairs away from the conference table.

We could not have anticipated the danger that awaited Monica and Carson as we followed the speeding S.W.A.T. team that sped silently towards Monica's G.P.S. signal.

Chapter Eighteen

Detective Lincoln was garbed in his bullet proof vest that read POLICE in bold yellow letters across the front. We waited back behind the police barricade as the S.W.A.T. team took their places around an abandoned building on Harry Hines. It was in a run-down area of Dallas, dimly lit, the unattended parking lot overgrown with weeds and littered with broken glass and debris.

The Captain of the S.W.A.T. team came over and updated Detective Lincoln. "We were able to thread a tactical mini camera through the roof and have an audio and visual feed on the female suspect. She is armed and holding two hostages at gunpoint," he updated Lincoln.

"Good job, Jacobs" Lincoln said and patted him on the back. "I want you to put Mrs. Spencer and Miss Lane in the control room. I think they might be able to help negotiate with our suspect," he instructed Captain Jacobs. He put on a headset with earpiece and microphone and began barking orders. "Let me know when everyone is in their positions," we could over-hear Lincoln instruct the S.W.A.T. team.

"Follow me, ladies," Captain Jacobs commanded.

We left Olivia, Cassandra, Shane and Sarah huddled safely behind the police barracades as Captain Jacobs ushered us into the mobile S.W.A.T. headquarters. The small interior was filled with computers, flat screen monitors, and a variety of machinery. Two officers were seated, studying the video feed and continually updating the team surrounding the building.

"Put these headsets on," Jacobs ordered and we immediately were able to hear the conversation between the officers as well as the audio feed from inside the building. Leslie and I both stared at the monitors and I was afraid to say anything into the microphone.

Lincoln could be heard over the P.A. system. "Holly Smith," he announced. "This is Detective Lincoln with the Dallas Police Department. We have the building surrounded. Come out with your hands up!" he shouted.

"Never. I will never surrender!" We heard Holly scream back at Lincoln.

"We are requesting you to release Miss Gold and Mr. Craig unharmed. Please send them out," Lincoln announced over the P.A.

"No. She ruined my life. Don't you understand? She took Carson from me!" Holly screeched from the abandoned building.

"Let's talk about this Holly," Detective Lincoln called out.

"I'm not falling for your games. What I want you can't give me. I want the life I was supposed to have. I want the life I was supposed to have with Carson. He was mine and she took him away!"

"She's not cooperating, Jacobs," Lincoln stated into his headpiece. "What's the status?"

"We've got a clear shot, Detective. Just say the word," the Captain could be heard saying over the police radio.

"We want to prevent casualties. Let's try to talk her out if possible. Let's get Amelia in contact with her," Lincoln stated.

"We need to keep her calm," Captain Jacobs instructed me. "We are going to call Miss Gold's cell phone and hope she picks it up. Try to talk her into letting the hostages go," he said in a reassuring tone.

I nodded in quiet affirmation as Monica's cell phone could be heard ringing over the audio feed. In the monitor, we could see Holly motion with her gun for Monica to hand her the cell phone.

"Holly, it's Amelia," I said as my voice trembled. "Holly, you don't want to hurt anyone. Please let Monica and Carson go," I implored her.

"I'm not letting them go. She was in on it," Holly yelled into the phone. "She covered up for her sister all these years. She helped that whore take him away from me!" she ranted.

"Holly, no one could ever love Carson like you do," I tried to reassure her. "Katherine didn't mean anything to him. She did the same thing to me with Jett. I know how you feel Holly, but think about what you are doing," I spoke into the headset.

"I know exactly what I'm doing. I'm making them all pay for ruining my life," she shouted into the cell phone. "What do I have? I have NOTHING and NO ONE to love me. She took the one man I truly loved."

"She seems to be getting more agitated," Leslie noticed. "Try talking to her about Gamma Phi," she suggested.

"Holly, think about what you are doing! You will ruin Gamma Phi Beta's reputation if you hurt them."

"I don't care anymore. Screw it all!" she screamed and snapped the cell phone closed.

"Captain, I'm in position to take the shot," an officer's voice could be heard in the headset.

We could hear Holly demanding over the tactical audio feed, "Tell me! Tell me you loved me more than her. Tell me you made a horrible mistake!" How could you love that whore?"

"Holly, Holly. Calm down!" Carson pleaded with her. "I never knew how you felt about me. Let's talk about this."

"You didn't know! You didn't know how I felt about you? How could you say that? I was totally devoted to you. How can you say you didn't know how I felt about you?" She was shrieking at him at the top of her voice.

"Oh, gosh, Amelia! She is crazy!" Leslie said and put her arm around my waist. "She sounds like she did that night at the sorority house."

"On my mark," Captain Jacobs ordered to his team.

"You men are all alike. You just want a quick jump in the sack. That's all I ever was to you!" Holly continued to accuse him.

So Carson had slept with Holly. No wonder why she felt so jilted when he turned to Katherine!

"Holly, we were just kids. We had been drinking. It didn't mean anything!" Carson told her.

"It meant something to me. It meant a whole lot to me!" She was livid now and her voice sounded like it was filled with so much venom.

"She couldn't be happy with every other man on campus. She had to take you from me too!" Holly shouted.

"Holly! There was never a you and me. We were drunk!" Carson pleaded.

"I was not drunk! I love you Carson and I loved you then. Don't you get it? No one could ever love you like I do. No one!" she began sobbing.

"Holly, put the gun down!" Monica could be heard telling her calmly. "Put the gun down before someone gets hurt."

"Shut up! SHUT UP, MONICA!" Holly screamed. "Don't tell me what to do!"

"Take the shot," Captain Jacobs shouted.

I heard gunfire and watched as the S.W.A.T. team kicked down the front door and flooded the building. I held my breath hoping Monica and Carson had not been injured. I watched as the E.M.S. workers rushed through the front entrance with a gurney. I took off my headset and grabbed Leslie's hand as we rushed out the door towards our friends huddled behind the police barricade line.

"Oh, gosh, Amelia! I hope Monica and Carson are okay!" Sarah said in an unsteady voice. "I will never forgive myself if something happened to her!"

"Sarah, sweetheart! Let's just pray everyone makes it out alive," Cassandra said and gave her a supportive hug. Sarah buried her head in Cassandra's shoulder and cried.

I stood in stunned amazement. I couldn't believe what had transpired today and I couldn't believe that Holly had been behind such a heinous murder! *How well do we truly know those around us?* I thought to myself.

Detective Lincoln walked out a sobbing Monica. We all rushed forward to embrace her.

"Oh, Monica! Are you all right?" Leslie said as she wiped a smudge of dirt off Monica's tear stained face. "I can't believe this happened to you!"

"I can't believe it either. One minute she was talking with me about Katherine and a memorial service on campus and the next minute she snapped and had a gun in my face! This has been a nightmare!" Monica said.

"We should have never left you alone!" Sarah told her and gave her a big hug. "We had no idea it was Holly!"

Just then a rather beat up and tired Carson Craig was wheeled out of the building on a gurney. He had a cut lip, black eye and what appeared to be several contusions on his head. He definitely had received the brunt of Holly's anger.

Jett rushed over to his side. "Carson, man it's good to see you!" he exclaimed.

"Brother, it's good to see you, too! I didn't think I was going to make it out of that one!" Carson said relieved.

"What happened, man?" Jett asked.

"She just snapped. She asked me to walk her to her car and when we got over to her mini-van she slid the back door open and she must have hit me pretty hard on the back of my head with something. I don't remember much of anything after that.

I guess she knocked me out. When I came to, I was tied up to a chair in this building," Carson recounted. "I have no idea what set her off!"

"I do, Carson." Monica stated as she walked over to the gurney. I told her that I thought Katherine's son should be at the memorial for her."

"Katherine had a son?" Carson asked incredulously. "I never knew that?"

"Yes. And he looks a lot like his daddy," Monica said and rubbed his arm. "He's nineteen years old and a sophomore at SMU. Katherine was moving to Dallas to be closer to him," Monica shared with Carson.

As Monica's news sunk in, Carson began to look around at the faces surrounding him. "Are you telling me that Katherine had a baby and it was MY baby?" he speculated.

"Yes, Carson. She knew that you were on your way to graduate school and she thought it would be best to not get in the way of your plans," Monica said as the tears rolled down her face. "I didn't agree with her not telling you, but she felt it was the best thing to do at the time."

"I have a son? I have a son!" Carson was starting to break down. "Katherine and I have a son," Carson wept. Monica leaned over and embraced Carson, the realization that Katherine was gone, the realization of the lost years of watching his son grow up and the realization that this hellish nightmare was over must have been just too much to bear.

We were all crying together. So thankful that Monica and Carson were okay.

Detective Lincoln walked over and shook hands with both Carson and Monica. He then came over to me and shook my hand.

Mrs. Spencer. I owe you a huge debt. If it had not been for your persistence in this matter, we would never have figured out the link with the missing tiara," Detective Lincoln told me.

I smiled at Detective Lincoln and gave him a big hug. "I think we're even. You saved my friend Monica's life. I will always be grateful for that," I told him.

"Well, this is an unexpected love fest over here," Olivia said as she approached us.

"And may I say it was an unexpected pleasure meeting you, Miss Rivers," Lincoln said as he shook Olivia's hand, their eyes locked, the electricity between the two almost visible. "If you are planning on extending your stay, I would be honored if you would allow me to escort you to this great place I know in Ft. Worth for some line dancing," he offered.

"Line dancing? You, the dashing Detective Lincoln line dances? This is just too good to be true!" Olivia laughed and threw back her head. "Here's my cell phone number. Why don't you call me tomorrow and we can take it from there?" She said and winked. She placed her business card in his hand.

"Ladies, Shane, Jett, it's been a pleasure. Duty calls. I'm back to work," Lincoln said and walked back over towards the crime scene, a big smile visible on his handsome face.

The E.M.S. workers carefully shut the ambulance doors. Carson was on his way to Medical City Dallas and we were on our way back to our hotel, tired and weary, but grateful things had turned out as good as they did.

Chapter Nineteen

A few weeks later, we flew back to Dallas for a Memorial Service for Katherine that was organized by the producers of "The Rich and the Lost." It was a private affair for friends and family held at Perkins Chapel on the SMU campus. A large tasteful portrait of Katherine was framed and placed on an easel at the front of the church. Large urns filled with yellow roses, Katherine's favorite, were placed on either side of her portrait.

Shane, Cassandra, Sarah, Olivia and I sat with Monica and her nephew, Craig. He did look much like Carson, but had his mother's smoldering eyes. Carson and his wife, Shelly, sat on the other side of Craig. Leslie could not join us since she was in the midst of filming Ron Howard's new movie.

The service was a very respectful tribute to Katherine and both Monica and Craig spoke about what a wonderful sister and mother she had been. There was not a dry eye in the church as Monica shared with everyone her stories of visiting Katherine at SMU during the weekends and what a wonderful job she had done in raising Craig.

Craig spoke about the unconditional love his mother had given him, privately sheltering him from the paparazzi and the Hollywood spotlight. She had sent him to good schools, traveled extensively with him and encouraged him to attend her alma-mater and to follow in his father's footsteps at SMU. She had explained to him that one day he would know his father, that the timing had been wrong, but to know that he was very much loved!

Craig had an opportunity to spend some time with Carson and Shelly in Dallas and had slowly been introduced to Carson's other children, Sam and Ryan. They were thrilled to have a big brother who played football at SMU. Now they had someone to throw the football with and someone to cheer on at games on campus. Carson and Craig were still getting to know each other, but so far, it had gone very smoothly. He was a great kid and Carson was very proud of him!

"Katherine did a great job raising Craig!" Carson told us as at the reception in Dallas Hall. "I just wish she could be here today to see us together," he said and proudly and looked toward his son.

"I think she's smiling down at you. She would be very proud to know how you and Shelly have welcomed him into your family," I told him and squeezed his hand.

"I'm glad to know that Katherine had a side to her that was soft and maternal. I never knew that side of her," he admitted.

It seemed so strange that after all this time, I was finally able to look back on my college years with a certain sentimental feeling. I no longer looked back at college as if everything that happened was a nightmare. We had all come out of it a bit scratched and bruised, but in the long run, everything had had a good conclusion.

Olivia walked over, hand in hand with Detective Lincoln. The two had been jet setting back and forth between Dogwood Cove and Dallas ever since their night of line dancing. It was good to see Olivia with someone who could not only stand up to her, but hold her interest as well. She deserved someone like Lincoln.

"What are you smiling about, Amelia?" Olivia asked.

"Oh," I said and sighed, "I was just thinking about coming full circle. I can't believe that Katherine brought us all together. For that, I'm thankful for knowing her."

"You seem distant, Amelia. What's up?" Cassandra asked as she crossed the marble floors of the rotunda of Dallas Hall, looking the part of best dressed diva in a gold Armani suit, in Katherine's honor.

"So much has happened since we left Dogwood Cove for the reunion. My head is still spinning," I told her.

Cassandra nodded. "Yes, I imagine you are tired from packing up the tea room."

"Not really. I didn't have to do much packing since Sarah bought it lock, stock and barrel," I said and smiled. I waved at Sarah who had brought Jack White with her for the trip. It seemed that owning "The Pink Lady" wasn't the only thing new in Sarah's life!

"I found a new friend," Olivia said looking up at Lincoln affectionately as the two walked over and joined us.

"Friends are we now?" Lincoln teased her. "That's not what you said last night as we were gazing out at the Dallas skyline."

"You hush, Lincoln, before I hog tie you!" Olivia said and smacked his arm lightly.

"Watch her, Lincoln," Cassandra laughed. "She means it!"

"Yeah, well hopefully she won't have any reason to hog tie me," he said and leaned over and gave her a kiss on the mouth. "I intend to keep you very happy," he said speaking to no one but Olivia.

"And how about you, Amelia? Olivia asked. "Are you going to take it easy for a while?"

"I think I will enjoy working with Shane on some new tea blends. I've got some great ideas for Smoky Mountain Coffee, Herb and Tea Company," I responded.

"Yes, yes she does," Shane said joining our little group. "I'm looking forward to having Amelia home for a while."

"Well, what about our chocolate and tea infused truffles? We've got to get started on those!" Cassandra reminded me.

"Yes, yes we do!" I cheerfully agreed with her.

"Chocolate and tea infused truffles? I love the idea!" Shane exclaimed.

"So do our Chefs at our kitchen in Paris. They want to meet with Amelia right away," she told him.

"How soon?" Shane asked.

"Shane, if I didn't know better, I would think you are trying to get rid of me," I accused him.

"Never. I think you need a change of scenery after all you have been through and Paris and recipe development would be just what the doctor ordered," Shane stated.

"What do you say, Amelia?" Cassandra raised her eyebrows hopefully. "What about next week?"

"Next week? Are you serious?" I asked. I couldn't believe she was even suggesting I pack for another trip again so soon.

"Next week will be fine, Cassandra. Now that we don't have to worry about the day to day running of 'The Pink Lady,' we have time for other things," Shane informed her. "Amelia will be happy to join you in Paris," he answered on my behalf.

"What about Emma and Charlie and school?" I asked him.

"We'll manage for a week or two and then school is out for Christmas break. Maybe we could join you in Paris for Christmas?" Shane asked hopefully.

Christmas in Paris? I couldn't imagine not being home for the holidays. But, Shane was right. Now that Sarah was running the tea room, I wouldn't have the busy holiday schedule with private parties, the extra cooking and decorating. I really wasn't sure what I was going to do to fill the time. I had been looking forward to a relaxing holiday at home with just the family.

"Well, I better finish my Christmas shopping then," I said and clapped my hands, starting the mental checklist of what I would have to do to get ready.

"What's all the excitement about?" Sarah asked as she and Jake walked up to us. She looked very un-costume-like today wearing a simple black jacket and matching pants. No hat, no big jewelry, no funky hairdo. I think Sarah was finding that she could express her creativity through her culinary presentations at the tea room. She was finally stretching her wings and running her own business and she seemed very satisfied!

"Amelia is going to Paris with Cassandra for Christmas," Olivia told her.

"Paris? Oh, how romantic! I've always wanted to go to Paris!" Sarah sighed.

"Why don't you then!" Cassandra suggested. "Why don't we all go to Paris?"

"Have you lost your mind, Cassandra? It's almost Christmas!" Olivia informed her.

"Yeah. So, take a break! Sarah, is 'The Pink Lady' going to be open during the holidays?" Cassandra asked.

"We will be closed December twenty-fourth through New Year's Day," Sarah said thoughtfully.

Cassandra turned toward Olivia. "What are your holiday plans?" she inquired.

"I don't know. I've got to take care of the farm. I wasn't planning anything special," she answered.

"Well, we can get the farmhands to cover for you and why don't you and Lincoln plan on joining us for Christmas and New Year's in Paris? I think it would be wonderful!" Cassandra said and was visibly excited about our new plans.

"Works for me!" Sarah said. "I'm sure it will be hard for me to get away for a while, but I'll manage," she said confidently.

"I'm in!" I told the group. "Definitely in!"

"Liv? We're waiting on you?" Cassandra pressured her. "Oh, come on! Those animals will be just fine without you for a while! What do you say?"

"I say, 'To the Traveling Tea Ladies' and to Paris!" Olivia said and we gave big hugs all around.

"You'll get used to it!" Shane told Lincoln as he shook his head side to side.

"Well, they are definitely not a boring group," Lincoln said as he smiled and put his arm around his little red haired spit fire. "Definitely not boring!"

~ THE END ~

HOW TO MAKE THE PERFECT POT OF TEA

In the same amount of time that you measure level scoops of coffee for the coffee maker and add ounces of water, you can prepare a cup or pot of tea.

Step One: Select your tea pot.

Porcelain or pottery is the better choice versus silver plated tea pots which can impart a slightly metallic taste. Make sure your tea pot is clean with no soapy residue and prime your tea pot by filling it with hot water, letting it sit for a few minutes, and then pouring the water out so that your pot will stay warm longer!

Step 2: WATER, WATER, WATER!

Begin with the cleanest, filtered, dechlorinated water you can. Good water makes a huge difference. Many of my tea room guests have asked why their tea doesn't taste the same at home. The chlorine in the water is often the culprit of sabotaging a great pot of tea.

Be sure your water comes to a rolling boil and quickly remove it. If you let it boil continuously, you will boil out all the oxygen and be left with a "flat" tasting tea. Please do not microwave your water. It can cause your water to "super boil" and lead to third degree burns. If you are in a situation where you don't have a full kitchen, purchase an electric tea kettle to quickly and easily make your hot water.

And NEVER, NEVER, EVER, MAKE TEA IN A COFFEE MAKER! I cannot tell you how I cringe when asked if it's okay. Coffee drinkers don't want to taste tea and tea drinkers don't want to taste coffee. Period! End of story! Golden rule—no coffee makers! Now, that we've cleared that up; let's measure out our tea!

Step 3: Measure Out Your Tea.

It's easy! The formula is one teaspoon of loose tea per 8 ounces of water. For example, if you are using a 4 cup teapot, you would use 4 teaspoons of tea, maybe a little less depending on your personal taste. Measure your tea and place inside a "t-sac" or paper filter made for tea, infuser ball, or tea filter basket. Place the tea inside your pot and now you're ready for steeping.

Step 4: Steeping Times and Temperature.

This is the key!

- Black teas—steep for 3–4 minutes with boiling water (212 degrees.)
- Herbals, Tisanes, and Rooibos—boiling water. Steep for 7 minutes.
- Oolongs—195-degree water. Steep for 3 minutes.
- Whites and Greens—steaming water—175 degrees. Steep for 3 minutes.

Over steeping any tea will make your tea bitter! Use a timer and get it right. Using water that is too hot for whites and greens will also make your tea bitter!

Got Milk?

Many tea drinkers are under the misconception that cream should be added to your tea, not milk. Actually, cream and half-n-half are too heavy. Milk can be added to most black teas and to some oolongs. I don't recommend it for herbals, greens and whites.

The debate continues as to whether to pour milk into your cup before your tea, or to add milk after you pour your tea. Really, the decision is yours! I always recommend tasting your tea first before adding milk or any sugar. You would be surprised how perfectly wonderful many teas are without any additions.

I think you're ready to start your tea adventure!

Until Our Next Pot of Tea,

Melanie

Recipes from
The Traveling Tea Ladies—
Death in Dallas

The Pink Dogwood Tea Room's Signature Peanut Butter Pie

"It's time to move on, Amelia," Shane said while taking another bite of my signature recipe peanut butter pie.

—*Chapter One*

- One 8 ounce block of cream cheese, room temperature
- 1 cup sugar
- 2 Tablespoons vanilla extract
- 1 cup creamy peanut butter
- 1½ cup of non-dairy whipped topping, thawed
- 1 chocolate cookie pie crust

Place cream cheese in a large bowl. Using an electric mixer, blend cream cheese and sugar until smooth. Add peanut butter to cream cheese mixture and continue to blend on high speed for one to two minutes. Add whipped topping and continue to blend until smooth and color is consistent. Pour into chocolate pie crust and refrigerate for six hours before serving.

*Garnish by drizzling with melted semi-sweet chocolate chips or mini peanut butter cups cut in half.

Note from Melanie: This pie has always been a tea room favorite and one most of our gentlemen guests asked for again and again. It was inspired by my peanut butter cup loving hubby, Keith.

Essie's Key Lime Pie

"Sarah, calm down!" Olivia scolded. "Amelia should be the one that's crying! You know she puts her heart and soul into everything she makes there. I know I am going to miss your Grandmother's Key Lime pie!"

—Chapter One

- One 8 ounce block of cream cheese, softened at room temperature
- 2 cans of sweetened condensed milk
- ½ cup key lime juice (fresh or bottled, NOT LIME JUICE!)
- 1 graham cracker pie crust

Place block of cream cheese in a large bowl. Using an electric mixture, whip cream cheese until smooth. Combine sweetened condensed milk and cream cheese on high speed until mixture is ultra smooth with no lumps. Add key lime juice and blend thoroughly. Pour into graham cracker crust and refrigerate for six to eight hours before serving. Garnish with a dollop of almond cream or fresh whipped cream and top with a mint leaf or slivered strawberry!

Note from Melanie: My grandmother, Essie, always made this pie when we came for a visit. She had a key lime tree in her backyard and would make this with freshly squeezed juice. Remember, REAL key limes are yellow and your pie should be a pale yellow, never fake green!

Southern Peach Iced Tea

I also had a key lime pie in a cooler in back of lady bug along with a gallon of my secret recipe peach iced tea. That surprise would be for later.

Amelia Spencer — Chapter One

- One cup sweet tea concentrate
- Three 11.3 ounce cans peach nectar
- ¼ cup fresh squeezed lemon juice
- Water

Pour peach nectar into a one gallon container or pitcher. Add ¼ cup lemon juice and one cup of sweet tea concentrate. Add water to top of container and stir until well mixed. Serve over ice!

Note from Melanie: This is my "Secret Recipe" and worth at least a million dollars! We had guests take gallons of this home, so beware if you make it once, you will always be asked to make it for every family get-together, Bunco night, PTA meeting. You get the picture!

Cassandra's Lynchburg Lemonade

"Wait a minute, wait a minute," Cassandra called out, her hands full of a pitcher of something icy. "I've brought the party; my own version of Lynchburg Lemonade."

—*Chapter One*

- 1 cup Jack Daniels whiskey
- 1 cup Triple Sec
- 1 cup sweet and sour mix
- 4 cups lemon-lime soda

Combine all four ingredients and serve over ice. Garnish with long stemmed cherry.

Note from Melanie: Lynchburg, Tennessee is worth a visit, even if you are not a fan of Jack Daniels. You can take a tour of the famous facility that put Lynchburg on the map!

Sarah's Fried Green Tomatoes

"Hey, Sarah," I jumped up and helped her with a rather large tray loaded down with all kinds of covered casserole dishes. "What have you got in here?"

"Oh, just my corn fritters, fried green tomatoes and potato salad," she announced, rather proud of herself!

—*Chapter One*

- 4 large green tomatoes
- 1½ cups buttermilk
- 1 tablespoon salt
- 1 teaspoon pepper
- 1 cup all purpose flour
- 1 cup cornmeal (self rising preferable)
- 3 cups vegetable oil

Cut tomatoes in ¼ inch slices. Place tomatoes in shallow dish and pour buttermilk over tomatoes. Sprinkle with salt and pepper. Combine flour and cornmeal in a shallow dish. Remove tomato slices from buttermilk and dredge each side of each slice in the cornmeal mixture. Heat vegetable oil in cast iron skillet on medium heat. Fry tomato slices in small batches until golden brown. Drain on paper towels and sprinkle with additional salt if desired. Best served hot.

Note from Melanie: Nothing is more southern than fried green tomatoes! Our area is famous for Grainger County tomatoes and we look forward to this seasonal delicacy each summer.

Tennessee Corn Fritters

She smiled at me and gave me a quick hug as I set down her assortment of covered casseroles and snuck a corn fritter while they were still warm.

Amelia Spencer — Chapter One

- 3 cups vegetable oil for frying
- 1 cup of all-purpose flour- sifted
- 1 teaspoon baking powder
- ½ teaspoon salt
- ¼ teaspoon granulated sugar
- 1 beaten egg
- ½ cup milk
- 1 tablespoon vegetable shortening, melted
- 1 can of corn kernels, drained or fresh off the cob (about 4 ears of corn)

Heat oil in deep pan or small counter-top fryer to 365 degrees. Careful, oil is hot and will spatter! In a bowl, combine flour, baking powder, salt and sugar. In a separate bowl, combine beaten egg, milk and melted shortening. Stir flour mixture into egg mixture until thoroughly mixed. Add corn. Drop batter by spoonful, CAREFULLY in the hot oil and fry until golden brown. Drain fritters on paper towel and serve warm. Makes 12 corn fritters.

Note From Melanie: Caution! These are addictive. You can sprinkle with powdered sugar and they become more of a sweet. I can remember my first corn fritter at The Kapok Tree Inn in Clear Water, Florida. I thought I had died and gone to heaven!

Amelia's Famous Almond Cream

I took the pie out of the cooler and sliced four healthy pieces. A little dollop of my famous almond cream and a sliver of strawberry on top; that should do it! I placed the pie and steaming mugs of coffee on one of Olivia's trays and joined the girls on the patio.

Amelia Spencer — Chapter One

- One pint heavy whipping cream
- ¼ cup confectioner's sugar
- 3 teaspoons almond or imitation almond extract

Place above ingredients in large bowl. Using an electric mixer on low to medium speed, whip all ingredients together until cream begins to thicken. Increase mixer speed to high and whip until soft peaks form. You can keep this refrigerated for up to one week. Simply rewhip before serving. It's perfect on scones, cake, pie, trifles and desserts. Good enough to eat alone!

Note from Melanie: I came up with this recipe on the fly when I was out of sour cream and vanilla extract needed to make "Mock Devonshire Cream." I looked in the pantry, and all I had was almond extract. It was such a hit, it was requested by our guests to take home. I would be strung up by my toe nails if I didn't have almond cream available!

Chocolate Chip Scones

I quickly washed my hands, slipped on my black and white toile apron and began preparations to make a quadruple batch of chocolate chip scones at the birthday girl's request. Sure, there are plenty of scone mixes out there that many other tea rooms used, but nothing was as good as making them from scratch. Yes, it was time consuming, but worth it!

Amelia Spencer — Chapter Two

- 2 cups all purpose flour
- ⅓ cup sugar
- 2 teaspoons baking powder
- 1 stick butter, chilled
- ½ cup semi-sweet chocolate chips
- 2 eggs
- 2 Tablespoons vanilla extract
- Heavy whipping cream or buttermilk — approximately ¼ to ½ cup (You will eyeball and add as needed)
- Cane sugar for topping

In a large bowl, combine flour, sugar, and baking powder. Cut butter into thin slices. Using pastry blender, cut butter into flour mixture until it resembles coarse meal. Add chocolate chips and mix. In a separate bowl, combine eggs and vanilla. Add to flour mixture and pour cream in a little at a time until mixture is sticky and dough forms. Just eyeball it and add just enough to moisten the dough. On a well floured surface, gently roll out dough to a ½-inch thickness. Flour a round biscuit cutter. Gently push straight down into dough and lift straight up. Do not twist cutter as that will break the air bubbles in the dough and you will not get a scones that is high. Place on baking sheet covered in parchment paper or silicone baking sheet. Sprinkle with cane sugar for a sweet and crunchy topping. Bake at 400 degrees for 23–25 minutes until slightly brown on top.

Note from Melanie: I recommend freezing for two or more hours to increase a nice rise and split of scones. Serve with almond cream, lemon curd or strawberry preserves. Before all my British readers contact me to tell me these are "not traditional" because of the chocolate chips, I dare you to try them! They are so moist, clotted cream and toppings are unnecessary!

Olivia's Lemonade Iced Tea

"Oh, the lemonade iced tea sounds perfect! Thank you!" And it was! Cold, slightly sweet and tart at the same time.

Amelia Spencer—Chapter Four

- 3 quarts fresh water
- 2 Large Luzianne Family sized tea bags—Yes, Luzianne! They are a blend of 3 black teas perfect for iced tea!
- ¾ cup of sugar or more depending on your personal taste
- One 12 ounce can frozen lemonade concentrate. I prefer Minute Maid.

Bring water to a boil. Place tea bags in the bottom of a gallon container or pitcher with tea tag draped over the side and secured. Pour boiling water over tea bags, just enough to cover. Place lid over container and allow to steep for EXACTLY 5 MINUTES! Remove bags and discard. Add thawed lemonade concentrate, sugar and cold water while stirring to dissolve lemonade and sugar. Refrigerate until ready to serve. Pour over ice and garnish with slice of lemon and sprig of mint!

Note from Melanie: This is the only bagged tea I serve in Miss Melanie's tea room and I use it specifically for our iced tea. Don't have Luzianne at your grocery store? Go to www.Luzianne.com to order yours! I promise I'm not their spokesperson, but you just can't beat this tea.

Green Tea Soaking Salts

He knew we would discuss this another time. A good soak in our antique deep claw foot tub could change any mood. I would just add a couple scoops of our aromatherapy line of green tea soaking salts with chamomile, lavender and peppermint and all my troubles and worries would be forgotten. Light a jasmine white tea candle, grab my favorite book and I would be set for relaxation! It was just what I needed.

Amelia Spencer—Chapter Three

- 1 cups sea salt
- 2 Tablespoons finely ground Sencha green tea
- 2 Tablespoons finely ground chamomile
- 2 Tablespoons finely ground lavender
- 2 Tablespoons finely ground mint leaves
- 12 drops lavender essential oil

Place salt in a glass or stainless steel bowl. Grind up spices with a spice or coffee bean grinder dedicated to aromatherapy only as this will interfere with flavors and aroma. Add essential oil and combine with a stainless steel whisk. Place in a glass jar with airtight lid. Store in cool, dry area.

Note from Melanie: To avoid a bit of a mess in your tub, fill cheese cloth, a fabric sachet or t-sac paper filter with tea salts. Drape from faucet and fill your tub with hot water. Now Relax! Tea bath salts can be customized with rose petals, white tea, and any combination of essential oils. Makes wonderful gifts!

Resources Guide

Here is a list of places to visit on the web or when you are visiting Dallas, Texas. I hope you will have fun creating your own "tea adventure" with these wonderful sights!

- **Smoky Mountain Coffee, Herb & Tea Company**: Official tea company of The Traveling Tea Ladies, (423) 926-0123, www.SmokyMountainCoffee-Herb-Tea.com

- **Lily The Porch Kitty Blog**: Official mascot of Miss Melanie's Tea Room, www.Blog.MissMelaniesTeaRoom.com

- **The Tea Academy**: Consulting and Training for Tea Professionals, (423) 926-0123, www.TheTeaAcademy.com

- **Miss Melanie's Tea Room**: 123 East Unaka Avenue, Johnson City, Tennessee 37601, (423)926-0123, www.MissMelaniesTeaRoom.com www.facebook.com//MissMelaniesTeaRoom

- **Southern Methodist University**: Dallas, Texas, www.smu.edu

- **Adolphus Hotel**: 1321 Commerce Street, Dallas, TX 75202, (214)742-8200, www.hoteladolphus.com

- **The French Room at the Adolphus Hotel**: Afternoon Tea, Thurs–Sat 3:00–4:45. For afternoon tea reservations (214) 742-8200 ext. 3174

- **Snuffer's**: 3526 Greenville Avenue, Dallas, TX. Best burgers and cheese fries ever! (214) 826-6850, www.Snuffers.com

- **Spa Habitat**: 3669 McKinney Avenue, Dallas, TX 75204. Voted "Best Spa in Dallas." (214) 522-9989, www.SpaHabitat.com

- **SMU Marching Jazz Band**: "Best Dressed Band in the Land!" http://people.smu.edu/band/Traditions.htm

- **Bubba's Chicken**: 6617 Hillcrest Blvd. Dallas, TX 75205, (214) 373-6527, www.Bubbascatering.org

- **Fans of the Traveling Tea Ladies**: Keep up-to-date with book signings, tea tours, recipes and more! www.TheTraveling TeaLadies.com or www.Facebook.com//FansOfTheTraveling TeaLadies

- **The Traveling Tea Ladies Society**: Register your group of "tea friends," share your tea travel adventures and pictures with us! Special opportunities to join Melanie for fun, fellowship and tea tours! www.TheTravelingTeaLadies Society.com or www.FaceBook.com//TheTravelingTea LadiesSociety

- **La Madeleine's**: 3072 Mockingbird Lane, Dallas, TX 75205, (214) 696-0800, www.LaMadeleine.com

- **Dakota's Restaurant**: 600 North Akard Street, Dallas, TX 75201, (214) 740-4001, www.DakotasRestaurant.com

- **The Rosewood Crescent Hotel**: 400 Crescent Court, Dallas, Texas 75201, (214) 871-3200, www.crescentcourt .com

About The Author

Melanie O'Hara-Salyers is a graduate of Southern Methodist University as well as East Tennessee State University. Her hobbies include travel, cooking for her large family, dancing, tea drinking, herb and flower gardening, reading and spending time with her husband, Keith, and their five children.

She enjoys working with local children, teaching etiquette and cooking through her "Kids in the Kitchen" classes and summer camps. Melanie also encourages children to develop a love of reading through her monthly "Literary Teas" that are based on classic novels such as *Little Women*, *Anne of Green Gables*, *Gone with the Wind* and *The Secret Garden*.

Melanie also shares her passion for tea with people inspired to follow their tea dreams. Participants in her Tea Academy seminars held across the U.S. and at her tea room, Miss Melanie's Tea Room, receive extensive training, tea education, and learn how to successfully own, operate, and promote their own tea businesses.

She is proud to call East Tennessee home. Her tea room, Miss Melanie's, and her online tea and coffee business, Smoky Mountain Coffee, Herb and Tea Company, is located in the heart of historic downtown Johnson City. If you would like to schedule a tea lecture, tea tasting, cooking demonstration, book signing or tea tour, please e-mail her at: Melanie@TheTraveling TeaLadies.com

About the Artist

Under the tutelage of James McCarty, her Wilmington High School art teacher, Pam discovered an aptitude and a love for portraiture. The school display cases often featured her work, and she sold her first painting to a member of the faculty. Fearing it would be an unsteady income, Pam did not pursue a career in art, but chose, rather, to pursue a degree in business.

While attending college, she worked as a secretary and supplemented that income with professional commissions — mainly, water color portraits of people and animals. She made the switch to oil paints when a friend gave her a starter set as a Christmas gift, and it quickly became her favorite medium.

In 1994, Pam became both a wife and a state licensed real estate appraiser. In 2002, Pam opened her own appraisal business in Southwest Ohio, but she also began dedicating time to painting. Since then, in addition to several commissions, she has done paintings for her own collection and has begun participating in local art and craft shows. One of her originals was recently purchased by Southern State Community College for their permanent collection.

Over the years, Pam's interests began to include graphic art, such as business logos and custom greeting cards. Encouraged by the local response to her greeting cards, and at the urging of a local librarian, she decided to take a look at writing and illustrating professionally.

To see more of Pam's work, please visit her website at www.pamkeaton.com

The Tea Academy
Consulting & Training For Tea Professionals
www.TheTeaAcademy.com

Smoky Mountain Coffee, Herb & Tea Company
www.Smokymountaincoffee-herb-tea.com
Official Tea Company of *The Traveling Tea Ladies*

Take a trip to Coleman, Virginia where pie is not the only dish served!

Mountain Girl Press author Lisa Hall takes a humorous, yet thoughtful look at the life in a fictional small Appalachian town. Her "Cutie Pie," series keeps heartwarming humor on the front burner!

Secrets, Lies, and Pies

In Coleman, Virginia, one can expect a generous helping of humiliated beauty queens, ex-jocks, outlaws, and Marlene Prescotts's legendary pie. Marlene is the beautiful and successful owner of a bakery called Cutie Pies. When the Coleman Canasta Club, better known as The Hens, set out to destroy Marlene's reputation with a malicious rumor, Marlene and her two best friends cook up the perfect plan to gain sweet revenge! *Secrets, Lies, and Pies* is the first in the Coleman, Virginia series.

Cheaters, Pies, and Lullabies

Return to Coleman for *Cheaters, Pies, and Lullabies*, the much anticipated sequel to *Secrets, Lies, and Pies*. Nothing that anyone does in this small town goes without notice. So, how long can cheating spouses commence to carrying on without being caught? How does a new mother cope with evil stares and nasty comments as her parenting skills come under attack? Readers will find the answers to these and many other questions in *Cheaters, Pies and Lullabies*.

Play Dates, Pies, and Sad Goodbyes

The end of *Cheaters, Pies, and Lullabies* left readers with lots of questions, and found some of the ladies in Coleman at a crossroads. Is Charity's marriage worth saving? Will Marlene sell Cutie Pies in order to stay home with her son?

Some life-changing decisions, a devastating diagnosis, and a family tragedy will forever change the lives of Marlene, Allison, Dorothy and Charity. If you are a fan of the "Cutie Pies," series, do not miss this opportunity to know the characters like never before.

A bit of sour, a dusting of sugar, and a sprinkling of tears will make the third book of the "Cutie Pies," series more tempting than a big ole' slice of Marlene's pie. You will want to dig in! Come back to Coleman for *Play Dates, Pies, and Sad Goodbyes!*

Coming in 2011

The Traveling Tea Ladies
Death in Dixie

Former tea room owner, Amelia Spencer, and her fun-loving friends are known about their small town of Dogwood, Tennessee as "The Traveling Tea Ladies" because everywhere their tea travels take them, murder and mayhem seem to follow. After a frantic call for help from good friend and owner of Lyla's Tea Room, Lucy Lyle in neighboring Jonesborough, Amelia and the girls decide to take a road trip to offer their assistance. Upon their arrival, they find Lucy in deep despair, her chef and most of her wait-staff having been lured away by new competing tea bar owner, Cheryl White, right before International Story Telling Festival and the arrival of thousands of tourists to Jonesborough. Small towns can hold big secrets and Cheryl White has made many enemies, so when she is found murdered and all signs point to Lucy, Amelia and the girls know it's up to them to discover the real killer.

Strong women, strong tea and even stronger friendships are steeped in this mystery. Snuggle up with your favorite pot of tea and prepare one of the delectable recipes from this page turner. *The Traveling Tea Ladies—Death in Dixie* will leave you screaming for MORE!

Breinigsville, PA USA
28 January 2011
254325BV00001B/23/P